Journeys

Burgoon

THEME 1

Journeys

Reader's Library Selection 1, *Sky*
To accompany Anthology Selection 1, *Akiak*
Comprehension Skill: Story Structure

Reader's Library Selection 2, *Elena in America*
To accompany Anthology Selection 2, *Grandfather's Journey*
Comprehension Skill: Author's Viewpoint

Reader's Library Selection 3, *Tommy Thompson's Ship of Gold*
To accompany Anthology Selection 3, *Finding the Titanic*
Comprehension Skill: Text Organization

Reader's Library Selection 4, *Race of the* River Runner
To accompany Anthology Selection 4, *By the Shores of Silver Lake*
Comprehension Skill: Noting Details

Elena in America

by Robin Bloksberg

illustrated by Sandra Speidel

Elena in America

by **Robin Bloksberg**

illustrated by Sandra Speidel

Strategy Focus

Will Elena be happy when she goes to America? As you read, try to **predict** how Elena will feel about her new home.

Responding

Think About the Selection

1. Where does Elena come from?

2. Why does Elena think about her village in Russia?

3. Does the author feel it is easy or hard to move to a new country? How can you tell?

What Does the Author Feel?

Copy the chart on a piece of paper. Then fill in details from the story that support what the author feels.

The Author Feels	I Know This from These Details in the Story
It feels bad to be a stranger.	The author says that being a stranger was no fun.
Having friends can make you feel good.	?
Having two countries can be nice.	?

When Elena was little, she lived in Russia. Russia is a very big country. Even so, Elena's own world was small. All she knew was the little village where she and her family lived.

Elena will always be a Russian girl. But she is also starting to feel like an American girl. Elena feels as if she has two homes — the one she left behind, and the beautiful one that she now loves.

Then, when Elena was nine, her father told her,
"Elena, we're moving to America."
When Elena's family first arrived in America,
they stayed with her uncle in Evanston, Illinois.
Evanston looked nothing like Russia!

Sometimes Elena dreams about Russia, her
beautiful country. She can still picture the river that
ran through the town where she lived. She can
remember the taste of the salted fish she loved so well.

Elena felt very shy when she went into town.
The people looked different from the people she knew
in Russia. Everything seemed strange. Elena felt like
a stranger. Being a stranger was no fun.

One night, Elena invited her new friends to
sleep over at her house. As a treat, her mother made
them dumplings filled with meat. The girls liked
them. Elena told them they were called *piroshki*.

Then, one day, Elena's father went to a nearby city. When he came back, he had a new job. "We're moving," he told the family — in Russian, of course. So Elena's family packed their things, again, and moved to Chicago.

As Elena's English got better, it was easier to make new friends. Some of the girls invited her to see a movie. Elena had not laughed so much since she had left Russia. She even understood most of it!

Some of the girls on the basketball team became good friends to Elena. When she made mistakes in English, they helped her learn to say things the right way.

Elena's father started his new job. Elena spent the rest of the summer exploring the city with her mother and sister. When they spoke Russian to each other, people would sometimes stare.

It was not easy getting used to her new home.

34

27

17A

Elena in America/Selection 2

In Russia, Elena had lived in a little town. There were few people. She knew everyone. In Chicago, there were so many people! Elena and her family didn't know anyone.

Elena wasn't sure she would be happy in America.

Ivan was a good friend, but sometimes Elena missed having girlfriends. Then she tried out for the basketball team.

She was very proud when she made the team!

She was even happier when the team members hugged her.

In September, Elena started school. She was very nervous. There were other children at school from different countries. A boy named Ivan was also from Russia! It felt wonderful for Elena to talk with him in Russian.

Another day, Elena's mother took her to eat hamburgers. They also had milk shakes and french fries. Elena loved the food! They didn't have places like this in her little village in Russia.

Elena in America/Selection 2

At Elena's school in Russia, she had had lots of friends. At her new school, Elena only knew Ivan at first. They did many things together. When Ivan was not around, Elena felt lonely.

Sometimes Elena went walking with her mother and sister. One day, they found a Russian grocery store! They bought some dark bread and delicious sausage, just like they used to eat in Russia.

TOMMY THOMPSON'S SHIP OF GOLD

by Anne Sibley O'Brien

illustrated by Paul Lee

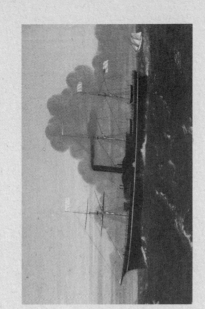

TOMMY THOMPSON'S SHIP OF GOLD

by Anne Sibley O'Brien
illustrated by Paul Lee

Strategy Focus

A ship full of gold lies deep at the bottom of the sea. Can Tommy Thompson find the treasure? As you read, **monitor** how well you understand each part of the story.

Responding

THINK ABOUT THE SELECTION

1 What was the *Central America* carrying?

2 Why did the girls think the miners from California had run out of luck?

3 How do the headings help you understand what you are reading?

TEXT ORGANIZERS

Copy the chart on a piece of paper. Then for each heading in the story, tell what happened in that part of the story.

Heading	What this part of the story is about
The Ship Sails, 1857	In 1857, the *Central America* sets sail.
The Storm	A big storm hits the *Central America*.
The Rescue	?

THE SHIP SAILS, 1857

On a sunny September day in 1857, the sidewheel steamer *Central America* set sail. She was heading from Cuba to New York City. She carried over 500 people. The *Central America* also carried gold—over one-and-a-half million dollars' worth!

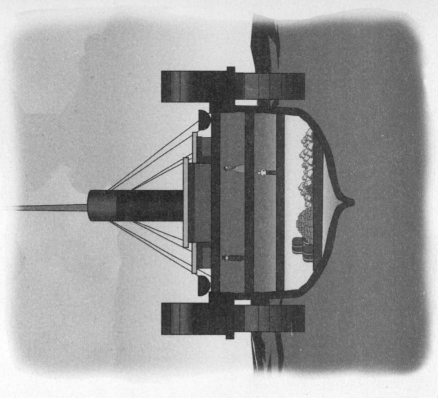

Tommy used a number of inventions to pull up all the gold and other things from the *Central America*. But for Tommy, the bigger treasure was how he had solved his problem. He had found a new way to uncover the secrets hidden deep at the bottom of the sea.

Tommy Thompson's Ship of Gold/Selection 3

Two nine-year-old girls traveled on the *Central America*. Their names were Harriet Lockwood and Augustine Pahud. On this bright day, the girls laughed and played on the deck in the sun.

TREASURE!

But most amazing of all, there was gold—thousands of gold coins and gold bars! Everywhere the ROV looked, there was gold. That first trip, the ROV pulled up just 40 coins. But Tommy would make more trips. Over time, he would pull up millions of dollars' worth of gold.

Everywhere they looked, Tommy's team saw gold.

THE STORM

Soon the skies turned dark. Wild winds started to blow. Powerful waves tossed the *Central America* like a cork. Harriet and Augustine ran inside to ride out the storm.

Before long, the crew was spreading the bad news. The *Central America* was leaking! People bailed water, trying to keep the ship from sinking.

Another ship, the *Marine*, had been spotted nearby. It was now on its way. But would it reach the *Central America* in time?

A photograph of a bell at the *Central America* wreck site, taken by *Nemo*.

Out at sea, the ROV worked better than Tommy had dreamed. On the first dive, it found the *Central America*! There were cups and plates and trunks of clothes. There were even books that could still be read.

54

LOOKING FOR THE CENTRAL AMERICA

✳

In the fall of 1988, Tommy and the *Arctic Discoverer* set sail to find the *Central America*. It would be the first time he used the new ROV. It had taken years of hard work and planning to get ready for this trip.

THE RESCUE

The *Marine* finally arrived. The *Central America* lowered her lifeboats onto the water. Harriet and Augustine went with the other children and women. The lifeboats set off through the waves for the waiting *Marine*.

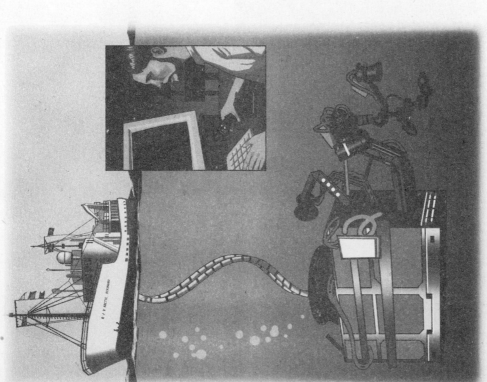

Tommy could run the ROV from a ship called the *Arctic Discoverer*. The ROV would send pictures from the ocean floor to the ship. It could also pick up things on the ocean floor — things like gold coins.

This painting shows how an artist in 1857 imagined the sinking of the *Central America*.

THE SOLUTION

By 1988, Tommy had made a new robot for exploring deep under the ocean. It was called a remote-operated vehicle, or ROV. Tommy could send it thousands of feet underwater to find the *Central America*.

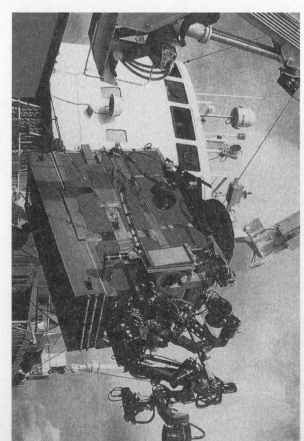

The ROV that Tommy and his team invented, called *Nemo*.

The Ship Sinks

When the girls arrived safely on the deck of the *Marine*, they looked back at the *Central America*. Several hundred men were still on board. Many were rich miners returning from the California Gold Rush country. The girls thought how luck was about to run out for these men.

After two days, the *Central America* went down. Over 400 people, mostly men, went with her. The *Central America* also took 42,000 pounds of gold to the ocean floor. It would be over 100 years before another person saw this treasure fit for a king.

The Problem

Tommy also knew the *Central America* lay over one mile below the sea. Even if he could find the treasure, Tommy could never bring it up from that far down. But Tommy had a plan.

one mile

THE EXPLORER, 1986

In 1986, Tommy Thompson was a smart young inventor who loved exploring the ocean. He dreamed of uncovering the secrets of the deep. Of all the ocean's secrets, shipwrecks interested Tommy most of all.

Tommy had heard about the *Central America*. He knew the ship had gone down with millions, maybe billions, of dollars' worth of gold. The gold would be much more valuable today than it had been in 1857. No one had ever found an underwater treasure that big.

Tommy Thompson stands on the *Arctic Discoverer*.

Race of the RIVER RUNNER

by Geoff Smith

illustrated by Winson Trang

Race of the RIVER RUNNER

by Geoff Smith
illustrated by Winson Trang

Strategy Focus

The captain of the *River Runner* takes Sun on an amazing journey. As you read, think of **questions** about the story that you might ask a friend.

Responding

THINK ABOUT THE SELECTION

1 What kind of boat was the *River Runner*?

2 How do you think Sun feels about Captain Skiddy at the end of the story? Why?

3 What details in the story make the steamboat race exciting?

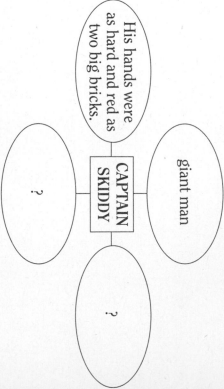

NOTING DETAILS

Copy this web on a piece of paper. Then add two more details that describe Captain Skiddy.

CAPTAIN SKIDDY

- His hands were as hard and red as two big bricks.
- giant man
- ?
- ?

S**un** L**iu** followed his father across the busy New York City docks. Horses pulled carts. Workmen carried heavy sacks. The great steamboat *River Runner* was about to sail up the Hudson River.

33A

The *River Runner* pulled up to Albany later that night. The moon sat fat and bright in the black sky. As he left the boat, Sun thanked the Captain for a story that he would always carry with him.

74

Race of the RIVER RUNNER/Selection 4

Sun's father was heading to Albany on business. At the last minute, he had asked Sun to come along. On board the ship, Sun's father went right to his room to work. But Sun set off to explore.

Sun zipped up the stairs to the very top deck. It was like standing on a mountain. The blue water sparkled in the morning light. Sun wished his father could see how beautiful it was.

"More steam!" Sun yelled. Something about
Captain Skiddy made him feel brave.

The *River Runner*'s engine roared. The rocks lay
straight ahead!

At the last moment, the captain spun the wheel.
The *River Runner* shot in front of the *Hudson Queen*.
The other boat turned into calm waters and slowed.

"I'd say we got her good," Skiddy laughed.

"I'd say so!" Sun cheered.

Race of the RIVER RUNNER/Selection 4

35A

"What's your name, sailor?" a voice boomed. Sun turned to see a giant man smiling right at him.

"I'm Francis Skiddy," said the man, "the pilot of this fine ship. Come on into my house."

"The best thing about life on a steamboat is that everyone is coming from or going to somewhere else," said Captain Skiddy. "What's your story?" His smile glowed like the buttons on his jacket.

As the *River Runner* pulled ahead, people on land stopped to watch. The sight of the two steaming giants fighting it out was too good to miss. A man rode his bicycle along the shore trying to keep up.

The *River Runner's* side wheel chopped the water. But the *Hudson Queen* chugged by her side.

"Rocks ahead!" Captain Skiddy suddenly yelled. "They're trying to get us to stop short! What do you say we do, Sun?"

Race of the RIVER RUNNER/Selection 4

37A

70

Sun explained that he had been born in China. But because of his father's work, his family had moved to London, then Boston, and now New York.

"I don't know where to call home," said Sun.

"I've lived on boats all my life. I'll tell you one thing I've learned," Captain Skiddy said. "Keep your eyes open and remember what you see, and you'll always carry your home with you."

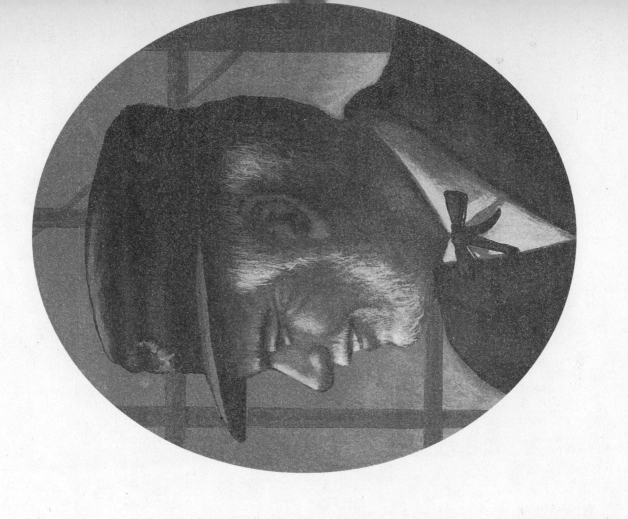

"Yes!" cried Sun.

Captain Skiddy sounded the whistle.

"Yell into that pipe," shouted the captain.

"Tell the engine room Full Steam Ahead!"

Sun stood on his toes and yelled. The engine began to chug.

Black smoke poured from the stacks of both boats. Orange sparks flew into the air. Huge wakes of water splashed along the shore. People on both boats cheered. The race was on!

Race of the RIVER RUNNER/Selection 4

Sun sat on an old, empty apple crate. The big man turned the boat's huge wooden wheel. His hands were as hard and red as two big bricks. As he steered, the captain told about life on the river.

Just before lunch another steamboat pulled up next to them.

"It's the *Hudson Queen!*" said Captain Skiddy. "She's as close to us as peel on an apple. Looks like she wants a race. What do you think, Sun?"

HOUGHTON MIFFLIN
Reading
A Legacy of Literacy

American Stories

THEME 2

American Stories

Reader's Library Selection 1, *The Math Bee*
To accompany Anthology Selection 1, *Tómas and the Library Lady*
Comprehension Skill: Sequence of Events

Reader's Library Selection 2, *A Breath of Fresh Air*
To accompany Anthology Selection 2, *Tanya's Reunion*
Comprehension Skill: Making Inferences

Reader's Library Selection 3, *Two Cold Ears*
To accompany Anthology Selection 3, *Boss of the Plains*
Comprehension Skill: Making Generalizations

Reader's Library Selection 4, *Two-Star Day*
To accompany Anthology Selection 4, *A Very Important Day*
Comprehension Skill: Categorize/Classify

The Math Bee

by Delores Lowe Friedman

illustrated by Bill Farnsworth

The Math Bee

by Delores Lowe Friedman
illustrated by Bill Farnsworth

Strategy Focus

When Portia competes in a school math bee, can you **predict** who will be her biggest supporters?

Responding

Think About the Selection

1. Where does Portia's father work?

2. What is the difference between a spelling bee and a math bee?

3. When does Dad give Portia his medal?

What Happens Next?

Copy the chart on a piece of paper. Write these events from the story in order on the chart:

Portia's team wins the math bee.

Portia and Dad go to the airport.

Portia gets chosen for the math bee.

Portia helps Dad with chores.

Story Events
1. Portia helps Dad with chores.
?
?
?

S

Saturdays were always busy at the Gordon house. Mom was up and out to work just as the sun began to fill the sky. When Dad woke Portia at nine, she pulled the covers over her head.

"Just let me sleep a little longer," she begged.

"Chores!" said Dad.

3B

Dr. Portia B. Gordon-Ketosugbo grew up in Queens, New York. She loved math as a little girl and enjoyed doing problems with her father, who was an award-winning aeronautical engineer. Her fourth-grade teacher encouraged math skills with contests and competitions. Portia decided to use her love of math in the field of chemistry. She is now the director of research for a major pharmaceutical company.

The Math Bee/Selection 1

4B

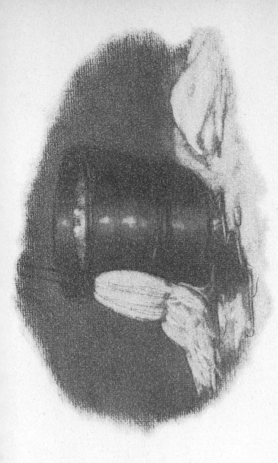

Portia did the dusting. Dad mopped the kitchen floor. Cleaning with Dad was fun because he always made up funny games to pass the time.

"Suppose you had four arms," he said, with a gleam in his eye.

"How many fingers would I have? Twenty," she said before Dad could continue.

"Good answer, but I was thinking you could dust two times faster, and you sure would be funny-looking." Dad said.

"Oh, Dad," Portia said with a sigh.

Just then the phone rang. Dad answered it.

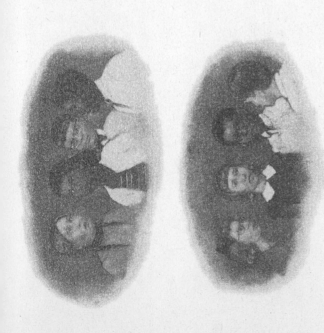

Portia stood close to her teammates on one side of the stage. The other fourth-grade team stood on the other side. The teams took turns solving problem after problem. Finally, the other team gave a wrong answer. If Portia and her teammates solved the problem correctly, they would win. The auditorium was very quiet.

Portia and her teammates worked out the problem. Portia called out the answer.

"That's right!" Mrs. Jackson shouted.

"Pizza party!" shouted Portia's class.

"Count me in!" said Portia.

When Dad hung up, he said, "Portia, I have to go to the airport. They're having some trouble landing the planes. Why don't you come with me?"

"Is it dangerous, Dad?" asked Portia. "Is a plane going to crash?"

"No, honey. I just have to look at some numbers and figure some things out," Dad answered.

At the airport they drove right to the control tower.

Inside were huge windows where the air traffic controllers could watch the planes they were guiding.

Then Dad took out a ribbon with a medal on it. "I want you to have this," he said.

"But Dad, this is your medal, and we haven't won the math bee yet."

"I think you have earned it," Dad said, "for all the hard work you did this month. When you work hard and do your best, you're a winner."

The next day, just before the contest, Miss Frew told the team, "You are ready. You studied hard. Just do your best, and you'll be winners!"

Just what Dad said! thought Portia.

"Look over there," said Dad as he pointed out a window. "A plane will land on that runway in exactly three minutes."

Portia looked back out at the runway. Before she knew it, there was the plane!

Portia said, "Wow, how did you know?"

"I knew how high up the plane was, how fast it was going, and how long it usually takes for a plane to land," answered Dad. "Just a big math problem, really."

The night before the math bee, Dad helped Portia do the hardest problems she had ever done. When she solved the last one, she asked, "Did I get it right?"

"What do you think?" he asked.

"I'm pretty sure I did. The answer just makes sense."

For the next several weeks, Portia got up early each morning. She hurried to school to work with three other students and Miss Frew.

Miss Frew taught them many math tricks and shortcuts. She taught them to do math problems in their heads and to work as fast as possible.

On Monday, Miss Frew told Portia's class, "Next month the school is having a math bee for the fourth-grade classes. It will be like a spelling bee, but with math problems."

I love math, Portia thought. I hope I can be in it.

"I think a team from our class can win," Miss Frew said. "If we do, we'll have a pizza party!"

14

11

The Math Bee/Selection 1

"That sounds great, Miss Frew," said Portia. "I want to be on the team, but I don't think I know how to win."

"That's okay," said Miss Frew. "I'll be your coach. The math team can come to school early every morning, and we can study together."

When Portia got home, Mom was in the kitchen. "How are you, sweetie?" she said.

"I'm great," said Portia. "We're having a math bee in school. Miss Frew said she would help us study."

"Your father won the math medal in high school. You should ask him to help you study, too."

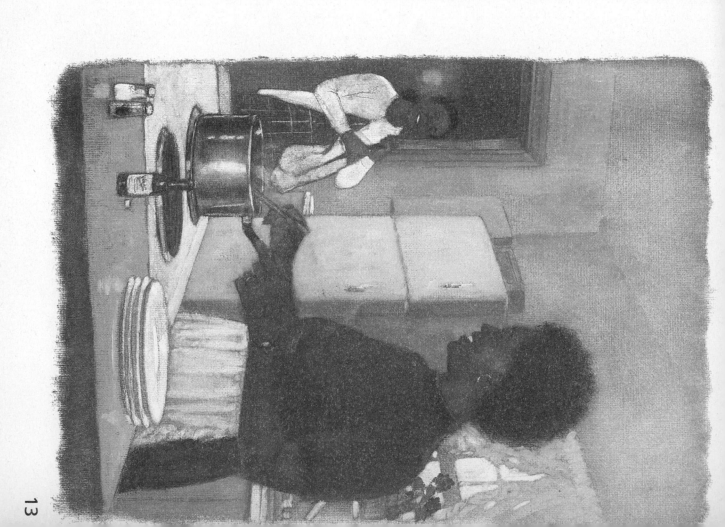

A Breath of Fresh Air

By Rhonda Rodriguez

illustrated by Cedric Lucas

A Breath of Fresh Air

By Rhonda Rodriguez
illustrated by Cedric Lucas

Strategy Focus

As you read about Javi's first trip out of the city, stop once in a while to **evaluate** how well the author shows Javi adjusting to country life.

Responding

Think About the Selection

1. Where do the Harrises live?

2. Name two clues that tell you this story happens many years ago.

3. If Ricky visits Javi, what might Javi show him in New York City?

Making Inferences

Copy this character study on a piece of paper. Read what the author says about the character. Then use the clues to write what you can figure out about the character.

Character Study for Javi Perez

What the author says:	What you can figure out:
Javi says "Thank you."	Javi is polite.
Javi can't sleep.	?
Javi makes a joke about cows.	?
Javi says he's the best stickball player on his block.	?

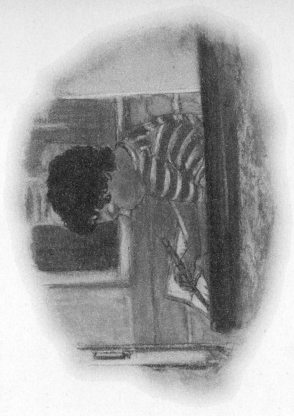

"July 7, 1959. Today I see the world," Javi Perez wrote in his diary.

Then Javi looked out the window of the train. It sped through the mountains, and all he could see were trees. He'd never been more than ten blocks away from his apartment before. But today he was traveling a hundred miles away from home to stay with a family he had never met. Javi was to be part of the Fresh Air program. It matched city kids with country families for two weeks during the summer.

Javi was in such a good mood by the end of the day that he forgot how much he itched. He even let Cypress lick him hello when he, Joey, and Ricky got home. "How about hamburgers for dinner tonight?" Mrs. Harris asked.

"YES!" said all three boys.

Javi smiled. He was going to like Northboro just fine.

Javi's mother thought he was too young to be part of the Fresh Air program. She didn't want him to go that far away. But Javi knew that age nine was old enough for an adventure. Just imagine, he thought. Two whole weeks of fun. He wouldn't have to help Mami do the laundry, babysit for his little sister, Rosa, or make sandwiches in Tía Lola's deli.

14B

They played stickball all afternoon. The other kids asked him lots of questions.

"Is it true that you can see all the way to Europe from the top of the Empire State Building?"

"Do you go to *all* the Yankee games?"

"Are you scared to ride on the subway?"

Javi couldn't believe it. They knew as little about New York City as he knew about Northboro!

The kids accepted Javi's dare. Before long, they had found a thick tree branch to hit with. They used their T-shirts as bases. Stu pitched the ball, and Javi slammed it out to left field, running the bases in record time.

"Hey, why didn't you tell us that you're the best stickball player in Brooklyn?" said Stu.

"Only the best on my block," said Javi, with a smile.

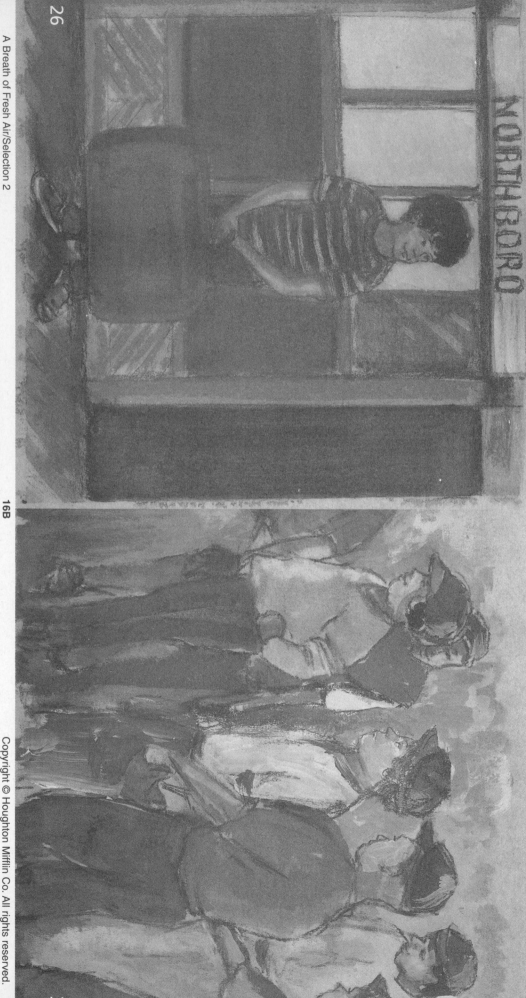

It was a long trip. Finally, the conductor called out "Northboro." Javi stepped onto the platform. The train pulled out of the station. No one was there to greet him. Have they forgotten about me? Javi wondered. Just then a station wagon turned into the parking lot. A woman leaned out the driver's window.

"Okay with me," Stu agreed. "But are you sure you want him? He doesn't even have a glove."

Javi scowled. He'd show Stu. "I don't need a glove!" he said. "I'll show you a REAL game we play back home in Brooklyn. It's called stickball. We don't need gloves or bats or anything."

"You must be Javi," she said. "I'm Marge Harris. I'm so glad you're here! Your room's all ready, and dinner's waiting."

"My own room?" Javi asked in surprise. Then he remembered his manners and said, "It's great to meet you, Mrs. Harris. Thank you for inviting me to your home."

"You are entirely welcome, Javi," Mrs. Harris said. "Your room is in the attic, but it's all yours. Now let's get home before the food gets cold."

Soon they were at a house with a yard even bigger than the Harrises'. A whole bunch of kids were there. An older boy named Stu was picking teams to play baseball.

"Put Javi on my team, Stu," Joey said.

The Harrises' front yard was bigger than the yards of five houses in Brooklyn put together. What do they do with so much space? Javi wondered. Then Mrs. Harris opened the front door, and a giant dog knocked Javi flat on his back and started licking his face.

"Cypress, get off now! Be nice!" Mrs. Harris said. The dog backed away, but Javi was still nervous. The dogs he knew in Brooklyn were half the size of this one.

The house was quiet. "The boys are still at Little League, but they'll be home soon," Mrs. Harris said. "Dinner's still warm. Have as much as you want. Do you want to eat in here or in the TV room?"

Javi blinked, not sure what to say. At home, his family ate dinner together. Mami made rice and beans, sometimes with chicken. Sometimes Papi brought home extra cod cakes from his job at the fish market.

19B

The next morning he woke up with several itchy, red mosquito bites. He went down to the kitchen. Mrs. Harris was having breakfast. She said, "Oh, Javi, the mosquitoes had a feast last night! Some lotion will take the itch away."

Soon, Javi had circles of crusty pink lotion on his face. He tried not to scratch them. He looked funny. He wanted to go home.

That afternoon, Javi followed Joey and Ricky down the road to town. They walked by a farm, and Javi held his nose. "What's that awful smell?"

"Haven't you ever seen a cow before?" Joey said.

"I've seen them, but I haven't smelled them," Javi said.

"Do you know why the brown cows are brown?" Ricky asked.

"Chocolate milk?" Javi joked.

They all laughed. "You're all right, for a city kid," Joey said, clapping him on the shoulder.

32

A Breath of Fresh Air/Selection 2

That night in his cozy attic room, Javi lay wide awake. At first he thought about the Harrises. They were so nice! He had met Joey, Ricky, and their father when they came home from Little League.

After a while, Javi tried to fall asleep. But it was too quiet. The only sound was crickets chirping. In Brooklyn, he could hear cars, radios, TVs, and conversations from the street. And Javi didn't know having a room of his own would be so lonely. Finally, he was so tired that he fell asleep.

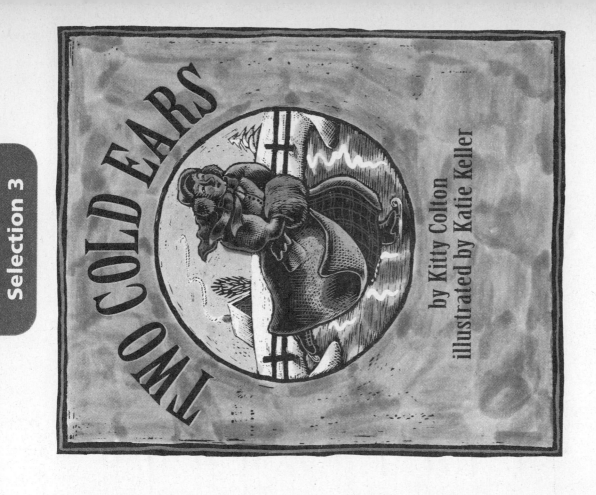

TWO COLD EARS

by Kitty Colton
illustrated by Katie Keller

TWO COLD EARS

by Kitty Colton
illustrated by Katie Keller

Strategy Focus

As you read, summarize each part of the story. Tell about what happens in your own words.

Responding

THINK ABOUT THE SELECTION

1 What did Chester call his invention at first?

2 How do you think Chester feels when he gets his new skates?

3 The author writes that nothing held Chester back. What does the author mean by "nothing"?

MAKING GENERALIZATIONS

Copy the chart on a piece of paper and answer the questions.

WHAT DOES THE AUTHOR MEAN BY "EVERYBODY" WHEN SHE WRITES	
Everybody in Farmington wanted a pair.	?
Everybody wears earmuffs, even dogs, horses, and fire engines!	?
Everybody laughed and pointed.	All of Chester's friends who were at the pond

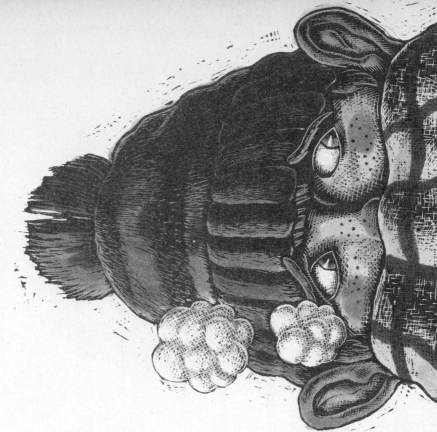

This is the story of how two cold ears lead to one big idea.

The ears belong to Chester Greenwood. Chester lived in Farmington, Maine, more than a hundred years ago. Some things were a lot different in those days.

Nowadays, Farmington is proud of its famous inventor. Every winter, folks gather to celebrate Chester Greenwood Day. There's an earmuff fashion show and a big parade. Of course, everybody wears earmuffs — even dogs, horses, and fire engines!

But other things were pretty much the same. Take the weather. From early fall to late spring, Farmington had only three kinds of weather: cold, colder, and coldest.

Chester built a factory to make his ear protectors. And Chester being Chester, he kept working to make them better.

He attached them to a bent strip of metal. He made the name better too. He called them "earmufflers."

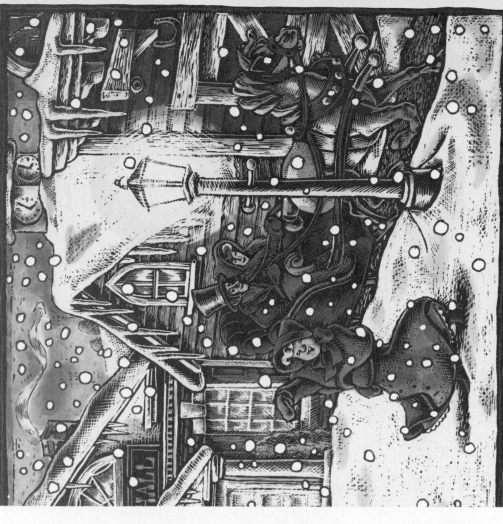

Chester loved the cold weather because it meant snow to sled on and ice to skate on. But there were two things about winter Chester didn't like at all: his ears.

25B

Well, as it turned out, lots of people wanted to wear Chester's ear protectors. Pretty soon, everybody in Farmington wanted a pair. Then people all over the world wanted them.

GREENWOOD'S CHAMPION EAR-PROTECTORS

54

You see, Chester had problem ears. They got so cold they ached. They turned colors, too — from white to red to blueberry blue. Hats didn't cover them. Wool mufflers made them itch.

Everybody laughed and pointed. "Who'd want to wear those silly things?" they shouted.

Chester tried everything he could think of. But nothing worked. No matter what he tried, his ears were always cold, colder, coldest. But cold ears couldn't hold Chester back.

Nothing held Chester back.

That boy was always bursting with smart notions.

As a young sprout, he did odd jobs for the neighbors. He gave the money he earned to his ma and pa.

45

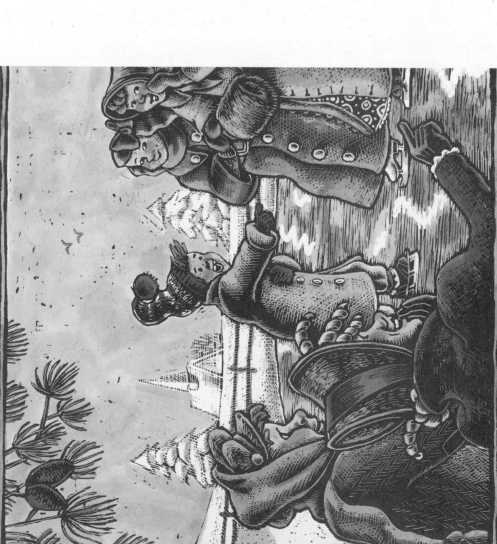

52

Back at Abbot Pond, Chester's friends called to him. "Hey, Chester! What have you got on your ears?"

Chester yelled back, "My ear protectors!"

When he was twelve, Chester sold eggs from his family's farm. He used the money to buy candy. Now, most kids would eat that candy. Not Chester. (Well, maybe a piece or two.) He sold it and gave the money to his family.

Chester put on the hat.
Ta-da!
His ears felt warm, warmer, warmest.
He raced out the door. He couldn't wait to try out his new invention.

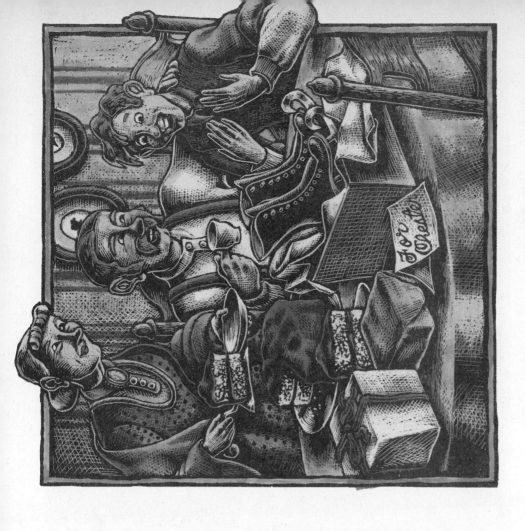

In 1873, Chester turned fifteen. His ma and pa gave him new ice skates. He rushed through his chores, and then he raced to Abbot Pond.

Chester found two pieces of wire. He bent them into circles. Then he found some scraps of fur and fabric. He asked his grandma to help him. She sewed beaver fur on the outside of each circle. On the inside, she sewed soft black velvet.

Then Chester hung the circles from his hat.

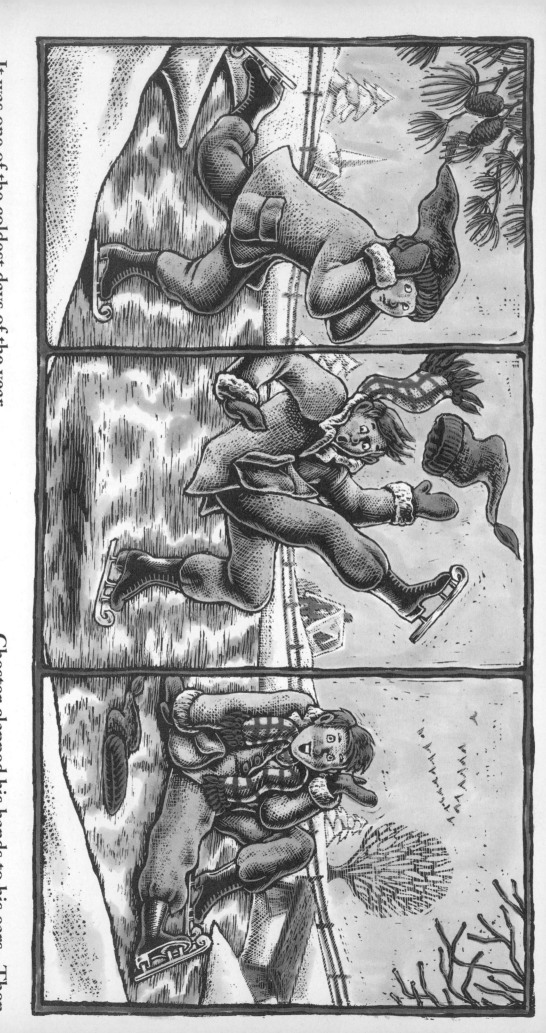

It was one of the coldest days of the year. The weather was swell for skating but not for ears. Chester yanked his hat down as far as it would go. He stepped on the ice. Right off, his ears started throbbing like toothaches.

Chester clapped his hands to his ears. Then he fell — splat! — on the ice. That's when the big idea knocked itself into his head.

As fast as he could, Chester took off for home.

Two-Star Day

by Veronica Freeman Ellis

illustrated by Garin Baker

Two-Star Day

by Veronica Freeman Ellis
illustrated by Garin Baker

Strategy Focus

It's a big day for Tonieh and his family. As you read, think of **questions** to ask Tonieh and his family about their day.

Responding

Think About the Selection

1. What country is Tonieh's family from?

2. How do you know Tonieh's family can now read and write English?

3. What happens because it is Tonieh's birthday? What happens because Tonieh's parents and sister are becoming citizens?

Categorize and Classify

Copy the chart on a piece of paper. Complete the chart by writing facts from the story for each category.

New Citizens Must:	New Citizens Over 18 May:
know history	vote
?	?
?	?

On Friday morning, Tonieh N'Da looked at the calendar on the kitchen wall. It was a two-star day.

That night, Tonieh felt lucky. Nine years ago, he was born a citizen of the United States. Next year, when he celebrated his tenth birthday, his family would celebrate their first year as citizens. It would be another two-star day!

Tonieh couldn't wait.

First of all, it was Tonieh's birthday. Second, it was the day his parents and sister would become United States citizens.

"I wrote about voting," said Tonieh's mother.
"I wrote about being on a jury," said his father.
"I wrote about people who become citizens," said Tanya.

Tonieh was already a citizen because he was born in the United States. His parents and sister were born in the Ivory Coast, in Africa.

61

"What did you read?" Tonieh asked.

"We read pages from a history book," said Tanya.

"What did you write?" asked Tonieh.

72

35B

People who become citizens must know United States history. So all winter long, Tonieh tested his family to get them ready for their citizenship ceremony.

"How many stars were on the first flag?" Tonieh asked.

"Thirteen for the thirteen colonies," his mother said.

"Why?" asked Tonieh.

"To show we can read and write English," said his father.

Francis Scott Key

"Who was the third president?" he asked.

"Thomas Jefferson," his father said.

"Who wrote 'The Star-Spangled Banner'?" Tonieh asked.

"Francis Scott Key," said his sister, Tanya.

Thomas Jefferson

"You were in that other room for a long time," said Tonieh.

"We took reading tests," said Tanya.

"We took writing tests, too," said Tonieh's mother. "Everyone who becomes a citizen takes those tests."

64

So now the day had arrived.

Tonieh waited with his family until they were called into another room.

Tonieh spent the time watching people come and go.

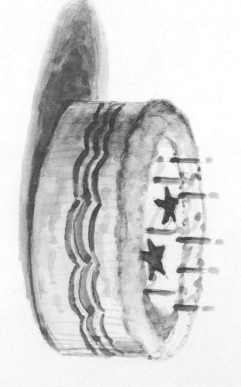

After the ceremony, the N'Da family went out for lunch. Everybody ordered their favorite dish. The best part was when the cake was served.

"Happy birthday to you!" said Tonieh's mother.

"Happy Citizen's Day to you!" said Tonieh.

69

Sometimes a man or a woman was called.
Sometimes it was a whole family. They all came
back holding a piece of paper.
At last Tonieh's family came back with theirs.

66

Now it was time to take the oath of citizenship. Tonieh stood with everyone as the judge entered. His family and the others raised their right hands. Now they were all citizens.

The judge spoke to the new citizens. She said that being a citizen of the United States is an honor. She told people over eighteen that they can vote. She said that citizens can serve on a jury and work for the government.

67

HOUGHTON MIFFLIN
Reading
A Legacy of Literacy

That's Amazing!

THEME 3

That's Amazing!

Reader's Library Selection 1, *One Day in May*
To accompany Anthology Selection 1, *The Stranger*
Comprehension Skill: Noting Details

Reader's Library Selection 2, *Tattercoat*
To accompany Anthology Selection 2, *Cendrillon*
Comprehension Skill: Compare and Contrast

Reader's Library Selection 3, *The Big Gust*
To accompany Anthology Selection 3, *Heat Wave*
Comprehension Skill: Fantasy and Realism

ONE DAY IN MAY

by Kitty Colton

illustrated by Kyrsten Brooker

ONE DAY IN MAY

by Kitty Colton
illustrated by Kyrsten Brooker

Strategy Focus

Spring is supposed to bring sunshine and beautiful colors. But all Lin sees is gray, gray, gray! As you read, **monitor** how well you're following the story events.

Responding

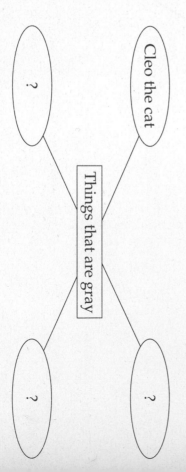

THINK ABOUT THE SELECTION

1. What color is Cleo the cat?

2. Why do you think the woman says the gray day is lovely?

3. What details show that the woman is unusual?

NOTING DETAILS

One way to understand how details are used by an author is to make a web. Copy the web on a piece of paper and write in details that the author uses to show how gray the setting is.

Cleo the cat

Things that are gray

?

?

?

Spring had come to the city. At least the calendar said so. There it was, in big, bold letters: May.

But when Lin looked out her window, everything looked gray.

The streets were soaked with sunshine. The city was bursting with the colors and sounds of spring.

Lin looked for her new friend, but she was gone. A patch of pink tulips had sprouted in her place. Cleo lay beside them, licking her sun-warmed fur.

20

3C

She saw no trees bursting with pale green buds. No candy-colored flowers poking through the ground. No bluebirds carrying twigs and leaves to line their nests. Not even a black-and-yellow bee.

All she saw was gray. Gray walls and gray roofs. Gray streets and gray steam rising from the grates. A patch of gray sky between the tall gray buildings.

"It really is spring!" Lin said. She ran up the stairs and into her house. She grabbed her brother, who was in front of his computer, as always.

"But I don't want to go outside!" he cried as they reached the doorway. "It's just a dumb old gray—"

She went outside, sat on her gray stoop, and sighed. She thought about spring at her old home, in the country. "I wish we'd never moved to the city," she said to her gray cat, Cleo.

A fat tear rolled down Lin's cheek. Cleo leaped off the stoop to chase a pigeon.

5C

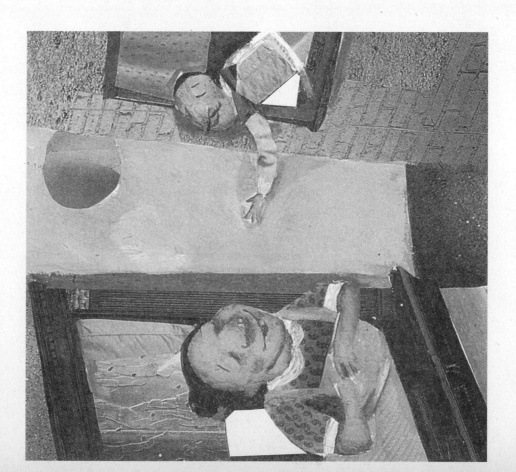

She paused and then added, half to herself, "But maybe there *has* been too much rain lately."

Just then, a bright burst of sun made Lin shade her eyes. Neighbors appeared on their stoops. They smiled and lifted their heads to the warmth, contented as Cleo.

18   ONE DAY IN MAY/Selection 1

"My my, you look like a storm cloud," said a sunny voice. Lin looked up, startled. A woman was sitting on the tree stump in front of her building.

"Huh?" Lin said, wiping her eyes. The city was crowded with people. But she had never seen anyone like this.

"Nature isn't just bright colors," said the woman. "Gray has its place too. Without gray skies and rain, there would be no flowers. And no worms to feed the baby birds."

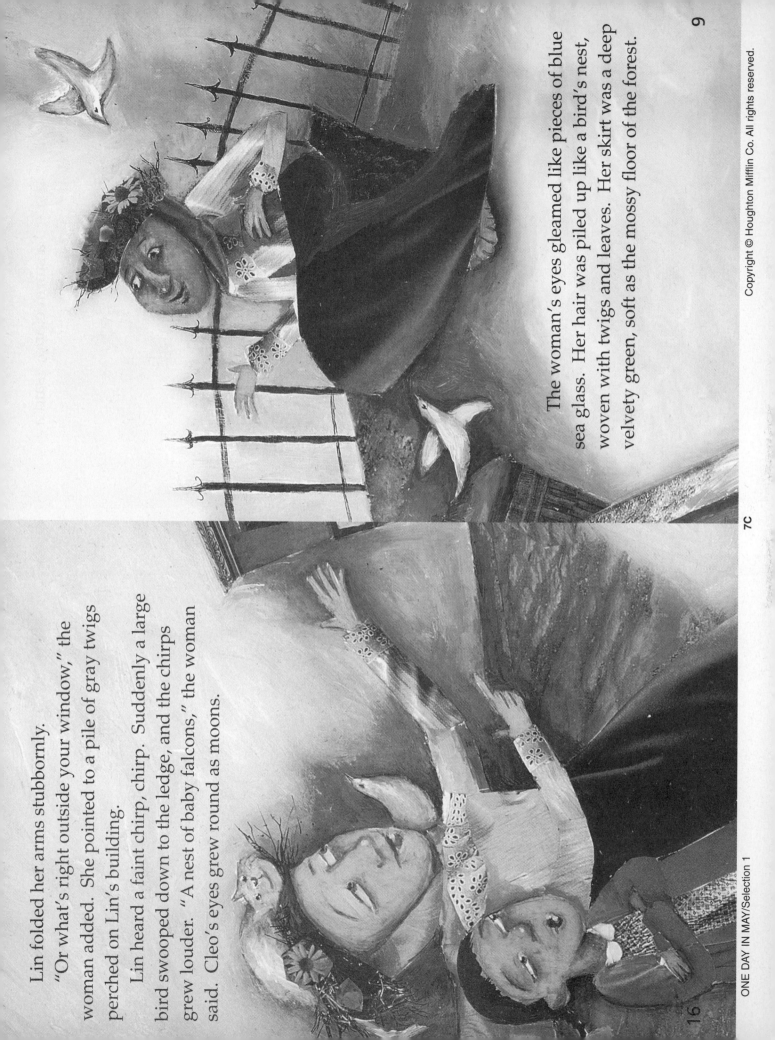

The woman's eyes gleamed like pieces of blue sea glass. Her hair was piled up like a bird's nest, woven with twigs and leaves. Her skirt was a deep velvety green, soft as the mossy floor of the forest.

Lin folded her arms stubbornly.

"Or what's right outside your window," the woman added. She pointed to a pile of gray twigs perched on Lin's building.

Lin heard a faint chirp, chirp. Suddenly a large bird swooped down to the ledge, and the chirps grew louder. "A nest of baby falcons," the woman said. Cleo's eyes grew round as moons.

16

Cleo stopped chasing the pigeon and stared. (Being a cat, she didn't care about being rude.) Then, to Lin's horror, Cleo jumped straight onto the woman's head.

The woman jumped to her feet and pointed down. A branch had sprouted up where she was sitting.

"Sometimes you don't notice what's right in front of your nose," she said.

"Oh!" Lin cried out, laughing. "I'm sorry. Cleo, you get down from there, you bad cat." But Cleo was already half buried in the woman's tangled mass of hair.

"No, that's purrrrr-fectly fine," the woman replied calmly, as if animals jumped into her hair all day long.

Lin shrugged and kicked at the stump.

"You shouldn't kick trees," the woman said gently. "They have feelings too, you know."

"But it's just a dead stump!" Lin said, and she kicked it again because that was the mood she was in.

Lin remembered that she was in a very bad mood. She started to scowl again.

"Tell me what's troubling you on such a lovely day," the woman said. Just then, the pigeon landed on her shoulder. "Helloooo!" she cooed at it.

"It's not a lovely day at all!" Lin said. "I hate the city. Back where I used to live, spring meant flowers and birds and blue sky. Here everything is just gray and dead."

The pigeon squawked loudly. "He says, 'What's wrong with gray?'" the woman told Lin. Cleo poked her head out and meowed her agreement.

12

13

Tattercoat
A Cinderella Tale from England

retold by
Susan Delaney

illustrated by
Kristen Bennett
Chavez

Tattercoat

A Cinderella Tale from England

retold by
Susan Delaney

illustrated by
Kristen Bennett
Chavez

Strategy Focus

Tattercoat's life gets off to a sad start. As you read, think of **questions** to ask about the lesson of the story.

Responding

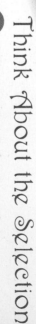

Think About the Selection

1. Who tells the story?

2. Why is Tattercoat treated so badly?

3. Compare Tattercoat's life before she meets the prince and her life after she meets him.

Compare and Contrast

Copy the chart on a piece of paper. Then check whether parts of *Cinderella* are the same as *Tattercoat* or different.

Cinderella	Same as Tattercoat	Different from Tattercoat
Cinderella wears dirty rags.	✔	
Cinderella is dressed up like a princess.		
Cinderella has a fairy godmother.		
Cinderella and the prince marry.		

I once knew a family whose house was filled with laughter and song. Their happiness spread like sunshine over the surrounding hills.

23

13C

Did they live happily ever after? Of course. I wouldn't have it any other way.

38

Then things changed, as things often do.
The daughter grew up and married a young
lord from a nearby village.

A year later, the couple had a baby girl. But
just after the child was born, the daughter died.
The family's joy died that day as well.

When we arrived at the ball, the prince
took Tattercoat's hand and led her to the king
and queen. "Father and Mother," he began,
"this is Tattercoat. Nowhere is there a kinder
or more loving girl. If she will have me, I wish
to marry her."

Tattercoat and the Prince danced joyfully
all night. Soon after, they were married.

36

Before the ball, Tattercoat rested beneath a
tall tree. I began to play my magic flute again
as she drifted off to sleep. When she woke up,
Tattercoat looked like a princess. Her rags had
changed to a deep blue gown, and on her once-
bare feet were sparkling silver shoes. She
blinked as she looked at herself.

"Am I dreaming?" she asked, turning to me.

"No," I said. "You just woke up from a long
nightmare."

25

Soon after, the young lord was called
away to battle. He wept as he kissed his
baby goodbye. But part of him was glad to
go to war. Perhaps on the battlefield he
could forget his sadness. The baby was left
in her grandparents' care.

But the grandparents wanted nothing to do with the baby. When they looked into her blue eyes, they saw only their lost daughter. They had no room in their hearts for love.

When the prince was gone, Tattercoat looked down at her clothes with a frown. "How could a prince ever care for a poor girl in rags?" she asked me.

But I knew that whoever fell in love with Tattercoat while my flute sang its magic did not see the rags she wore. Instead, he saw the goodness in her heart.

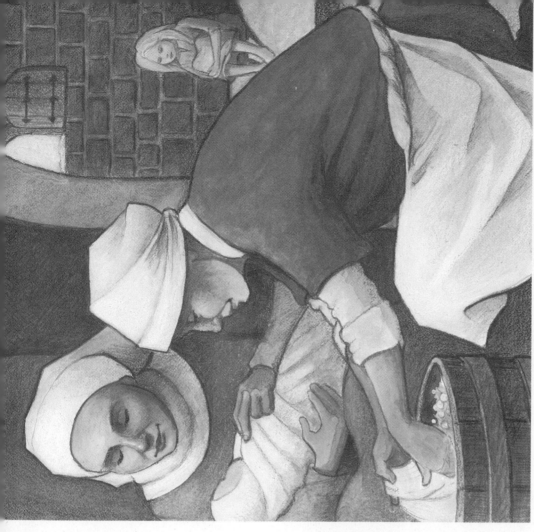

When the child was older, the grandparents put her in their servants' care. But the servants had children of their own, and no time or love to give to another. So they treated the child badly.

34

"I am the king's son," he said. "I'm on my way to my father's ball. Won't you please come as my guest? I must see you again." Tattercoat's eyes shone with joy. She nodded her head shyly.

The prince galloped off on his horse, shouting back, "Until tonight!"

27

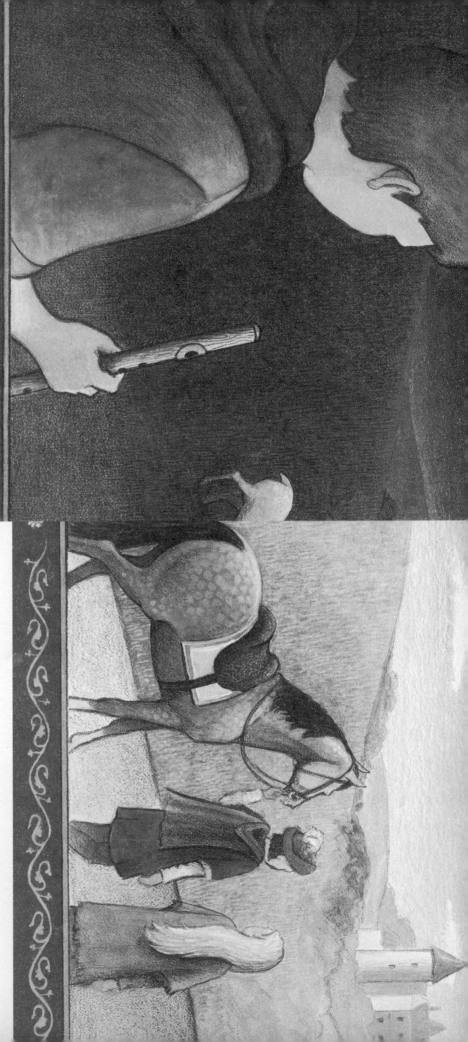

The servants called her Tattercoat, because the coat she wore was torn and ragged. She lived on crusts of bread and rinds of cheese. She slept in the dampest, coldest corner of the house.

When we neared the castle, the young man turned to Tattercoat. "Do you know who I am?" he asked.

"No sir, I'm sorry. Should I know you?" answered Tattercoat.

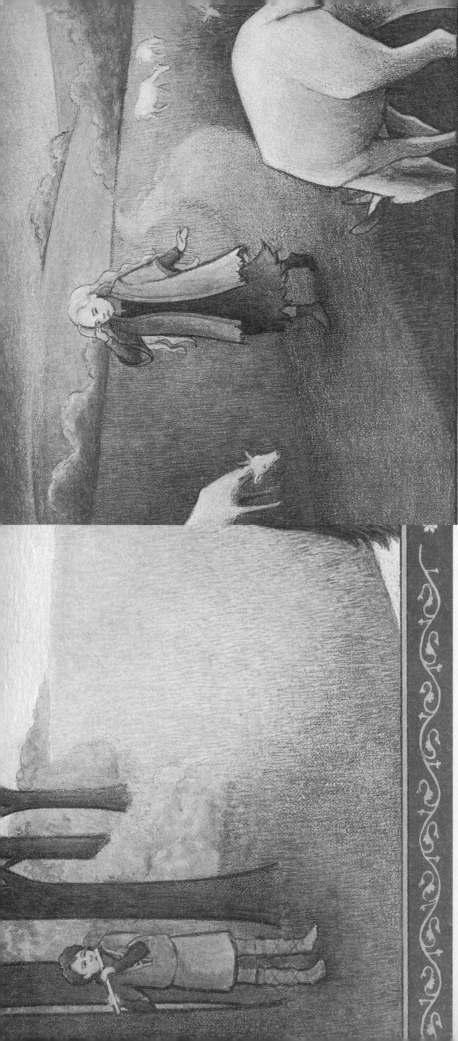

As we walked, a young man on a gray horse came up beside us. "Do you mind some company?" he asked. "I've been traveling a long way by myself."

The stranger and Tattercoat talked and laughed all the way to the castle. I had never seen her look so happy. I lagged behind, playing a tune on my flute.

32

The girl accepted all this with good grace. She quietly did whatever the servants told her to, and she never complained.

But when evening came, Tattercoat spent hours wandering the hills behind the house. That's when I first heard her sobbing.

29

19C

And that's when I became Tattercoat's one true friend.

20C

Time passed, and Tattercoat grew into a graceful young woman.

On the day the king was to give a ball, she told me, "Oh, I wish we could go. I imagine a ball is like the music from your flute, beautiful and magical all at once."

"Perhaps if we stand outside the castle, we can hear the music drift through the windows," I said. Tattercoat's face lit up with excitement. So we began the long walk to the palace.

THE BIG GUST

by Andrew Clements
illustrated by Terry Widener

THE BIG GUST

by Andrew Clements

illustrated by Terry Widener

Responding

Think About the Selection

1 Who is watering her garden when the big gust comes?

2 What does the caller tell the police?

3 What is the barking balloon, really? How does she get that way?

Fantasy/Realism

Copy this chart on a piece of paper. Then write things from the story that could really happen and things that could not.

What Could Happen	What Could Not Happen
Wind blows a kite through the air.	Wind blows a boy holding a kite through the air.
?	?
?	?

As fast as it came, the big gust left town. But the folks in Mayville will never forget that windy day.

Strange things have happened since then. But nothing has been as wild as that one big gust!

56

It was just another day in Mayville. Folks were doing the things that they did in the summer. And then that one big gust came through.

Everyone in Mayville knows where they were at the time.

41

Jean Adams had a dog named Clipper. Jean often said, "That name is perfect for my dog. I always have to clip her hair and nails."

When the big gust came, in fact, Clipper was getting clipped. She was also yawning. The wind blew into her mouth.

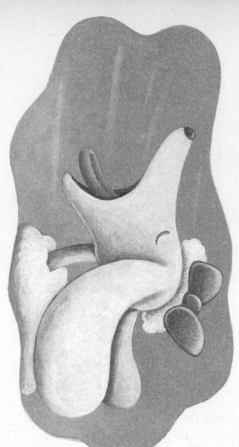

After that, Gary tried to build fences by juggling pickets, nails, and his hammer. As you might guess, he became a better juggler than a fence builder. So he joined the circus when it came to town.

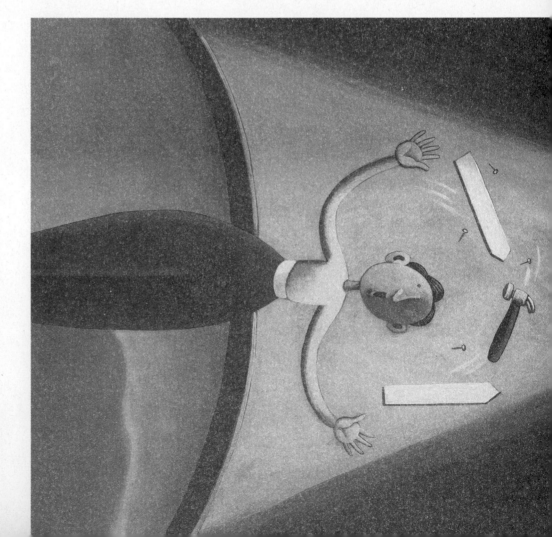

Clipper blew up until she was ten times bigger than before. Then away she went. Jean went after her.

It wasn't long before the police got a call. "Help! I'm being chased by a barking balloon with hair ribbons!" yelled the caller.

Gary Jones was all set to fix his picket fence. When the big gust came, every single picket and a whole box of nails went up in a jumble. But when they came down, Gary had a new fence. And he'd never even picked up his hammer!

54

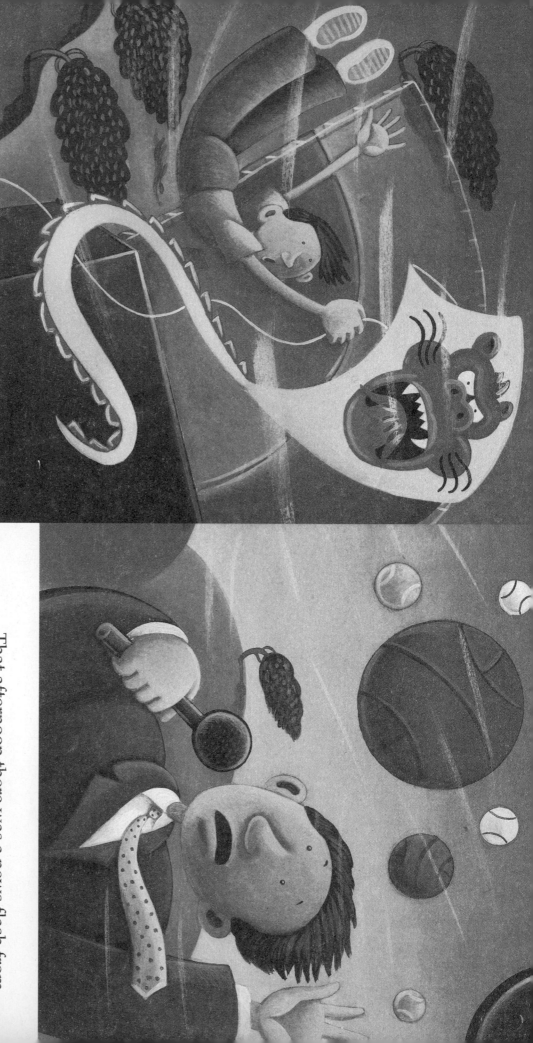

Tommy James was flying his new kite at the ball field. When the big gust came, Tommy held on tight. He went on a wild kite ride to the schoolyard.

That afternoon there was a news flash from Chestertown. "Tim Lewis here in the middle of a hailstorm. Some hailstones are as big as tennis balls. I mean softballs. No, wait a minute. . . . footballs! Could they be as big as bowling balls? Oh no, BASKETBALLS! HELP!"

Tommy saw the flagpole. He looped his legs and then the string around it. Then he slid down to the ground. He was safe and sound, but he had to leave the kite behind.

Over at the Sport Shop, Jane Asher was putting some tennis balls on the shelf. When the big gust came, they blew off the shelf and then blew all the way to Chestertown, along with other balls of all shapes and sizes.

Elsie Chen was watering her garden. When the big gust came, it swept the hat off her head. Elsie turned around to see where her hat went.

When she turned back, her garden was on the roof of the house next door.

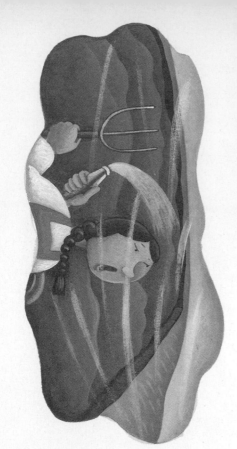

The big gust blew all the grass Bob mowed to the town library. It formed a pile on the front steps. Soon a bunch of kids were reading their books on that soft, delicious-smelling green carpet.

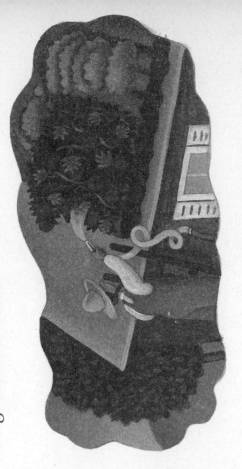

"Oh, good," thought Elsie. "Now my tomatoes are closer to the sun. I'll just get a longer hose and a tall ladder from the hardware store. I wonder if my neighbors will mind."

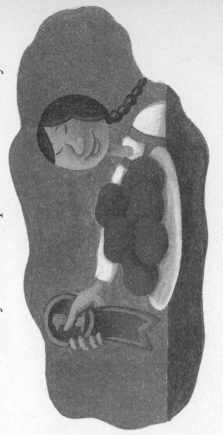

They didn't. Elsie's tomatoes got a lot of sunshine, water, and special attention up on that roof. Then they won first prize at the county fair!

47

Bob Belcher was mowing his lawn. When the big gust came, Bob and his mower took off like a driver and a racing car.

Together they cut a path through six front yards and a blackberry thicket.

50

At the school gym, some kids were playing kickball. When the big gust came, the doors flew open. You'll never guess what blew in. It was a pond, with three ducks, six lily pads, three frogs, and one tall man in a little red rowboat!

The tall man stayed to play water polo with the kids. The ducks and frogs watched the game from the red rowboat. The lily pads just sat there, taking up space.

HOUGHTON MIFFLIN
Reading
A Legacy of Literacy

Problem Solvers

THEME 4

Problem Solvers

Reader's Library Selection 1, *The Best Fish Ever*
To accompany Anthology Selection 1, *My Name is María Isabel*
Comprehension Skill: Predicting Outcomes

Reader's Library Selection 2, *Cora at Camp Blue Waters*
To accompany Anthology Selection 2, *Marven of the Great
  North Woods*
Comprehension Skill: Problem Solving

Reader's Library Selection 3, *Murals for Joy*
To accompany Anthology Selection 3, *The Last Dragon*
Comprehension Skill: Drawing Conclusions

Reader's Library Selection 4, *Ruthie's Perfect Poem*
To accompany Anthology Selection 4, *Sing to the Stars*
Comprehension Skill: Story Structure

The Best Fish Ever

The Drama Club
is having tryouts for

The Fisherman and
His Four Wishes

November 17   3:30 PM

by Julio Varela

illustrated by Eric Velasquez

The Best Fish Ever

The Drama Club
is having tryouts for

The Fisherman and His Four Wishes

November 17   3:30 PM

by Julio Varela
illustrated by Eric Velasquez

Strategy Focus

Manny just knows he will get the lead in the school play. As you read, use clues from the story to **predict** what will happen.

Responding

Think About the Selection

1. What play will the Drama Club present?

2. How does Manny feel about his tryout?

3. What prediction does Mr. Greene make that turns out to be right?

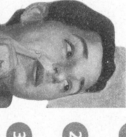

Predicting Outcomes

Copy this web on a piece of paper. Then write details from the story to support it.

The story title is "The Best Fish Ever."

?

Prediction: Manny will NOT play the fisherman in the play.

?

?

Too Excited to Eat

It was only 7:30 A.M., but Manny was almost out the door. Ever since he started fourth grade three months ago, he had been waiting for this day to come.

"Mom, don't forget," Manny called on his way out. "Today after school I'll be with the Drama Club. We're having tryouts for the play."

When the play ended, Manny heard nothing but cheers.

Mr. Greene told everyone that the play was a success because of their efforts. "I hope you'll all try out for the play next year."

"I know I will," Manny said. "But can I play a person next time?"

The Best Fish Ever/Selection 1

"I know, I know," Manny's mom said. "You've been talking about it for the last three months. You're not having breakfast?"

"I'm too excited to eat," said Manny. "See you later!"

"Good luck!" Manny's mom said as she closed the door.

As he waited for the elevator, all Manny could think about was the tryouts.

This year Mr. Greene, the drama teacher, turned the story "The Fisherman and His Four Wishes" into a play. The play had only three main characters — the fisherman, his wife, and the magic fish who could grant wishes.

The Play

Six weeks had passed, and the first performance of "The Fisherman and His Four Wishes" had finally arrived. It seemed as if the whole school was there. As the curtain rose and the play began, Mr. Greene looked proudly at his actors. He was right — Ahmad was a great fisherman. Everyone in the audience thought so the moment he walked on the stage.

But on that afternoon, the audience's favorite was the fish. Manny flopped around the stage and said his funny fish lines. He did just what he told himself over the past six weeks. "If I have to be a fish, then I'll be the best fish ever!"

Mr. Greene wrote a happy ending for the play. When the fisherman loses everything because of his foolish wishes, the fish feels sorry for him and grants him a *fourth* wish. Luckily, the fisherman has finally learned his lesson and wishes for something of real value.

It was going to be a great play. More than anything, Manny wanted to play the part of the fisherman.

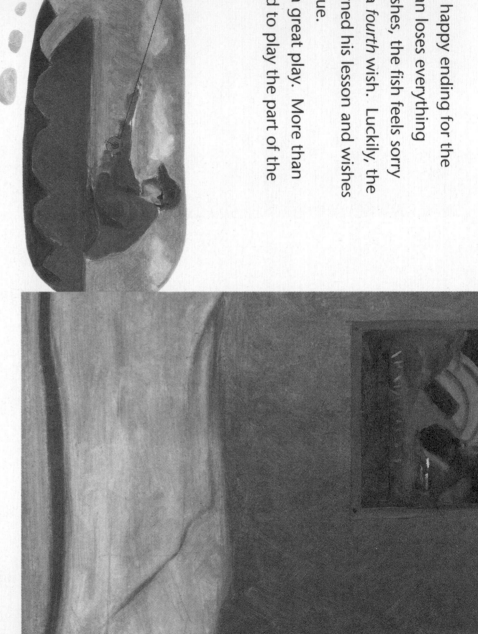

"Yeah, I'll think about it," Manny grumbled. "Good night."

Who Will Be the Fisherman?

"Mr. Greene says I would make a good fisherman," Manny said to his best friend, Nick. Nick looked up from his tuna sandwich. He took a sip of milk before talking to his friend.

"Are you forgetting something? You still have to try out. I mean, everyone wants to be the fisherman. Marcus, Guillermo, Richie, Ahmad, even Elena," Nick said.

As he got ready for bed, Manny told his mom what had happened. "It's just not fair," Manny said.

"Manny," said his mom, "just think about what Mr. Greene said. You want to be in the play. You're lucky to have been chosen."

"I know, but come on, you know I'm the best," Manny said. "I already know all the lines."

"I still think you should wait until you try out. What if you don't get it?" Nick asked.

"Yeah, right," Manny said, as if there were no chance of disappointment.

Nick shrugged his shoulders and went back to his sandwich.

"The *what?*" Manny yelped. "But Mr. Greene, I *really* want to be the fisherman. I know all the lines."

"So do a lot of the other kids," said Mr. Greene. "I gave that part to Ahmad. I think he'll make a great fisherman. *You* are going to make a great fish. Besides, the fish has the funniest lines in the play."

Mr. Greene took a deep breath and went on. "Manny, you are lucky. Lots of kids won't even be in the play. If you'd rather not play the fish, I'm sure I can find someone who will."

Manny didn't know what to say, and for a moment he was quiet. He then said good-bye to Mr. Greene.

10

15

The Tryouts

After school, Manny sat with the other Drama Club members and listened to Mr. Greene's instructions. "Okay, everyone, thanks for coming. When I call your name, please join me in the other room. You'll read your lines to me in there."

"Too bad," Manny thought. "Everyone but Mr. Greene will miss my tryout performance."

The Drama Club
is having tryouts for

**The Fisherman and
His Four Wishes**

November 17   3:30 PM

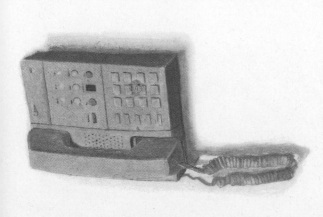

The Telephone Call

That night Manny sat at the kitchen table, trying to do his math homework. But all he could think about was Mr. Greene announcing, "Manny Rodríguez will be the fisherman."

Suddenly, the phone rang, jolting Manny from his daydream. It was Mr. Greene. "Manny, you did a good job today, and I've decided to give you the part of . . ."

"This is it, Manny thought. Say it's the fisherman.

". . . the fish."

First Mr. Greene called Elena, then Marcus, Richie, Guillermo, and Ahmad. Finally he called, "Manny Rodríguez."

Manny bolted from his seat, looked around to see how many others were waiting, and shouted, "Yes, sir, I'm ready!"

Mr. Greene gave Manny a script. Then he said, "Okay, Manny, in this scene you will read the part of the fisherman, and I will read the part of the fish. This is when the fisherman makes the wish to live in a castle. Ready? Let's go."

Manny began to read his lines. He knew every one of them by heart. This was too easy.

Cora at Camp Blue Waters

by Philemon Sturges

illustrated by Lori Lohstoeter

12D

Cora at Camp Blue Waters

by Philemon Sturges
illustrated by
Lori Lohstoeter

Strategy Focus

Cora is going to summer camp, even though she doesn't want to! As you read, **evaluate** what Cora does to solve her problems.

Responding

Think About the Selection

1. Who is Cora's cousin?
2. At the beginning of the story, what is Cora's problem with the outdoors?
3. How is Cora's problem solved?

Problem Solving

Copy the chart on a piece of paper. Read about camp leader Anne's problem. Write any solutions you read about in the story. Can you think of any others to write?

Anne's Problem	Solutions
It's a rainy day at the camp.	• Have the children dress in rain gear and take them out anyway. • ? • ?

Cora was an indoor girl, a homebody. Her favorite hobby was drawing. She mostly drew the ideas in her head. "I like to use my imagination," she said.

After she got home, Cora kept drawing outside as much as she could. One snowy day, as she sat indoors drawing the beautiful ideas that lived in her head, she noticed that the outside had come in.

Sometimes people encouraged her to draw something from real life, such as animals, trees, or flowers. "You need to get out more," her mom said.

"It's more interesting in here," she told her mom, pointing to her own head.

In fact, Cora hardly noticed what was around her at all, except for what she called "the yucky things" — bugs and snakes.

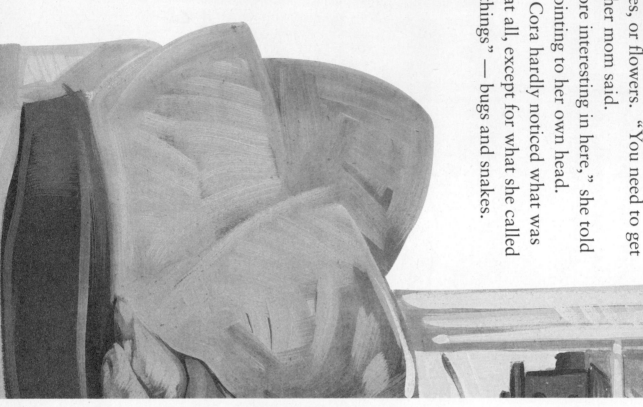

Now when Cora drew outdoors, she wasn't bothered by poison ivy, or thorns, or bugs. She was too busy noticing the blue petals that matched the color of the sky. And when she saw sticks that looked like snakes, she wished they *were* snakes, so she could draw them.

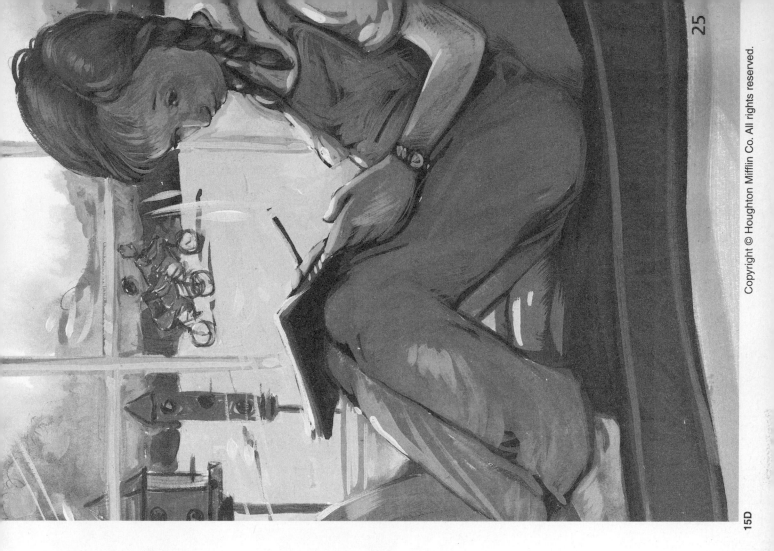

15D

Bill showed Cora how to choose colors
that matched nature. He taught her to see
shapes and patterns in the leaves, and how to
make living things look round on flat paper.
He taught her to draw flowers, bugs, fish, and
a rabbit she saw on the lawn.

When Cora showed Bill her drawing of
two robins in a twisty old apple tree, he called
her a "real wildlife artist."

Cora At Camp Blue Waters/Selection 2

"But why?" Cora asked, the first time they went out. "I have plenty of ideas in my own head. I don't need to look at things outside."

But Bill told her, "An artist always uses what's inside, even when she draws outside. Just give it a try! I'll be there to help."

So Cora was less than excited when her dad said that she'd be going to Camp Blue Waters that summer.

"Why me?" wailed Cora.

"Mom and I think you'd like the great outdoors if you'd give it a chance," said Cora's dad. "Besides, it's only for two weeks. Your pens and paper will be here when you get back."

"Your cousin Teri's going too! She went to Camp Blue Waters last summer, and she loved it," said Cora's mom. "You told me you never get to spend enough time with Teri. Here's your chance."

27

17D

Cora *did* go to the arts and crafts room every day. But she didn't stay there. Bill often told everyone to pack up their paper and pencils and paints and go outside.

34

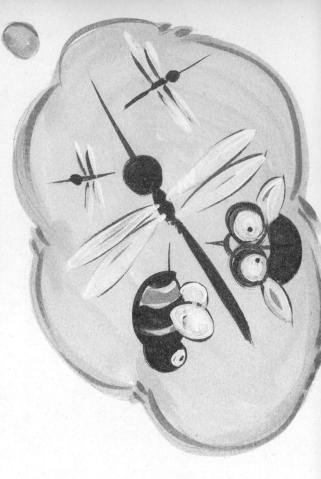

Cora couldn't fall asleep that night. She kept thinking about what was waiting for her at Camp Blue Waters. (Cora's imagination helped her draw, but it didn't help her sleep.) Ugh, thought Cora. I'm going to spend the next two weeks sweating and itching in the hot sun. Even the thought of being with Teri didn't help.

Anne opened the door and said, "And this is the arts and crafts room." It was filled with big tables and easels. There were boxes of pencils, paints, and scissors. And there were shelves of paper, all kinds of paper.

"And this is the arts and crafts teacher, Bill," said Anne. Bill gave the girls a friendly wink.

Neat, thought Cora. Now if I could just stay in this room for two weeks. . . .

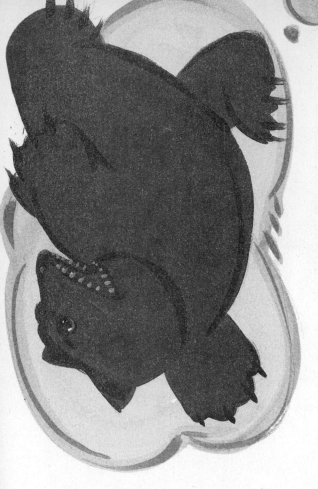

Cora didn't sleep well during her first night at Camp Blue Waters, either. Things weren't quite as bad as she thought they'd be, but there *were* flies buzzing near the screen, and there *was* a spider in the shower. Moths flew around and around the light outside her cabin door. Owls hooted in the trees. Even Teri made noises in her sleep. And Cora just knew there was a bear nearby.

32

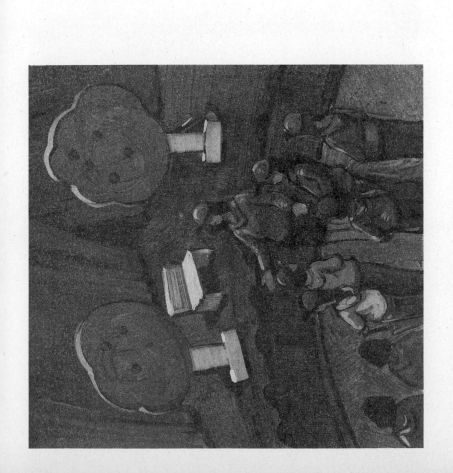

Anne said, "Let's get out of the rain for a little while." She led the girls to a large building. Inside was a huge room with a stage at one end and folding chairs at the other.

"This is where we put on plays and concerts," she said. Then she led them to another room.

The next morning, it rained. Still, Cora and Teri's camp leader, Anne, took everyone outside for a tour of the camp.

They passed smooth playing fields and softly rolling hills. They saw a still, dark lake with a pale, sandy beach. Then they walked through the deep, green woods.

But all Cora saw was poison ivy, thorns, and sticks that looked like snakes. When she jumped away from one especially snaky stick, she slipped on some wet grass and fell into a muddy puddle.

Cora was nearly in tears when Anne and Teri pulled her up.

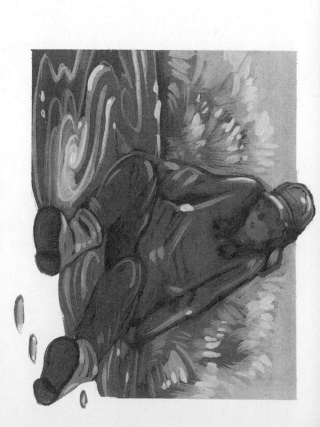

Murals for Joy

by Veronica Freeman Ellis

illustrated by Colin Bootman

YOUTH CENTER

Murals for Joy

by Veronica Freeman Ellis

illustrated by Colin Bootman

Strategy Focus

Joy doesn't think she'll have a good time in the city. As you read, stop once in a while to **summarize** what has happened.

Responding

Think About the Selection

1 Why does Celia like to sit on the apartment building steps?

2 Why do you think the director asks for ideas to stop the writing?

3 What clues in the story tell you that Joy's feelings about her summer in the city are changing?

Drawing Conclusions

Copy the chart on a piece of paper. Read the conclusion. Then complete the chart by writing two more clues that lead to the conclusion.

Clues	Conclusion
They have a meeting to figure out how to clean the walls.	The community is proud of the appearance of their Youth Center.
?	
?	

Celia and her mother, Mrs. Delaney, lived in the city. Every summer Celia visited her cousin Joy. Joy lived near the seashore with her parents.

When Celia visited, the girls played on the beach and swam. Sometimes they went sailing with Joy's parents.

"You're going home in two days, Joy," said Mrs. Delaney. "I know," said Joy. "Four weeks went by quickly."

"I'm sure you'll be back next summer," said Mrs. Delaney.

"Maybe she won't," said Celia.

Joy smiled and said, "Maybe I will."

This summer was different. Joy was spending four weeks with Celia in the city.

The girls sat outside Celia's apartment building.

"Is sitting on the steps all you do?" asked Joy.

"No," answered Celia, "but it's fun watching people."

"The murals are wonderful," said Mrs. Delaney when they were finished. "The center looks even better than it did before."

"Yes, it does," agreed Ms. Howard. "And I hope people will be too proud of these important African-Americans to write on their faces!"

Joy worked with others on the mural of Toni Morrison. Celia helped with the mural of Wynton Marsalis. Then they worked together on the mural of Martin Luther King, Jr. One Saturday, Mrs. Delaney worked with them on the mural of Duke Ellington.

"I don't think it's fun," grumbled Joy.

"If we were at my house, we'd be swimming, or we'd be sailing around the bay."

"City people do different things for fun," said Celia. "After four weeks, you may like what we do."

"Maybe I will," said Joy. "Or maybe I won't."

The next day the girls went to the Youth Center. "This is my cousin," Celia told the other children. "She'll be coming to the center with me this summer."

The group leader, Ms. Howard, invited Joy to join them in the day's activities.

First, everyone helped to paint over the writing. Then neighborhood artists drew pictures of the important African-Americans everyone had agreed on.

Then everyone helped the artists to paint in the outlined pictures.

Ms. Howard told the children they would be talking about important African-Americans. Later they would make posters of the people they liked and wanted to learn more about.

In the afternoon Ms. Howard helped the children make sweet potato pie. They ate the pie at snack time.

"Mmmmmm," said Joy. "This pie is dee-licious!"

Joy waved her hand, but the director didn't see her.

Mrs. Delaney stood and said, "Joy wants to speak."

"Let's paint murals that show important African-Americans," said Joy. "Murals will make it hard to write on the walls."

Everyone liked Joy's idea and agreed to paint murals.

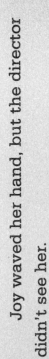

That evening Mrs. Delaney asked, "Joy, did you have some fun?"

"Not much," mumbled Joy. "I'd have more fun at home."

"Why don't you take her back home, Mom?" asked Celia.

"Give her time," said Mrs. Delaney.

"Maybe she'll like the city."

"Maybe I will," said Joy. "Or maybe I won't."

When Mrs. Delaney and the girls sat down, the center's director began to speak.

"Of course, we'll paint the walls," she said.

"But what about later on?" asked Ms. Howard. "Those who wrote on the walls will do so again."

The director asked for ideas to stop the writing.

The next day, Ms. Howard talked about Frederick Douglass, who fought slavery. She also talked about the musicians Duke Ellington and Wynton Marsalis and the writer Toni Morrison. Joy thought their lives sounded interesting and exciting. She asked many questions when Ms. Howard finished.

A crowd was outside the Youth Center on Saturday morning. Everyone was talking at the same time.

"What's going on?" asked Mrs. Delaney and the girls.

"Somebody wrote all over the center's walls," Ms. Howard answered.

"How awful!" exclaimed Joy. "What can we do about it?"

"We're having a meeting in the auditorium now," said Ms. Howard. "Please join us."

That evening Joy said, "Aunt Nancy, will you please take us to the library?"

"Certainly," said Mrs. Delaney. "What books do you want?"

"Books on Toni Morrison," answered Joy. "And the musicians Duke Ellington and Wynton Marsalis. Ms. Howard told us about all of them today."

Celia and Mrs. Delaney looked at each other and smiled. They were happy something interested Joy.

"Tomorrow's Saturday, so I don't have to work," said Mrs. Delaney. "We'll spend the morning at the library."

"Sounds good, Mom, but can we go to the center first?" said Celia. "I left my good sweater there yesterday."

Ruthie's Perfect Poem

by Andrew Clements

illustrated by Raul Colón

Selection 4

Ruthie's Perfect Poem

by Andrew Clements

illustrated by

Raul Colón

Strategy Focus

Ruthie is too shy to read her poems out loud. As you read, ask **questions** about how she will overcome her shyness.

Responding

Think About the Selection

1. Who is Ruthie's favorite author?
2. Why do you think Ruthie is so shy?
3. How do you think Ruthie feels at the end of the story?

Story Structure

Copy this map on a piece of paper and then complete it.

Title	*Ruthie's Perfect Poem*		
Characters	Ruthie	?	?
Setting	*Where*	?	
	When	?	
Beginning	Ruthie likes to daydream and write poems. But she is shy about sharing them with anyone.		
Middle	?		
End	?		

Ruthie Carter loved to imagine. She looked at a mud puddle, and she saw an ocean. She looked at a bookcase, and she saw a skyscraper.

But when Ruthie looked at herself, she saw nothing — just a shy girl who scribbled poems in a secret notebook.

Ruthie's mom said, "Your dad and I are so proud of you!" Her grandma gave Ruthie a big hug. Then she said, "I heard every single word, loud and clear."

Ruthie said, "That's because I read my poem just for you!"

Ruthie didn't like it when people looked at her. She kept her hair down in front of her eyes. That way she had a place to hide.

Ruthie never raised her hand in class, even when she had the right answer. When the teacher asked her to read out loud, Ruthie pretended she had a sore throat.

When Ruthie stopped reading, it was quiet —but just for a second. Then everyone clapped, and some people even stood up and cheered.

Mary DeLaney said, "You read that poem perfectly!" Then she gave Ruthie a new book and a gold ribbon.

When it was time to work in groups, Ruthie looked down at her shoes, hoping she wouldn't be picked for one. That way she could work all by herself.

Ruthie shook hands with Mary DeLaney and then started to read.

My Couch

Each Saturday at half past three,
My old gray couch says, "Come with me."
I stretch out flat, I close my eyes.
The couch lifts off the floor and flies!

Out we go, then over trees,
Beyond the hills, across the seas.
We fly through jungles green and deep.
I see the tigers crouch and creep.
We fly above the desert sands.
I wave at camel caravans.

It's wonderful to feel so free,
But something always puzzles me.
It matters not how far we roam,
By dinnertime, we're always home.

72

35D

Ruthie's Perfect Poem/Selection 4

One day Ruthie's teacher said, "Mary DeLaney is coming to visit our school." Ruthie couldn't believe it. Mary DeLaney wrote wonderful poems and stories. She was Ruthie's favorite author!

The next night, a nervous Ruthie sat with her mom and dad and grandma at the assembly. When Mary DeLaney called her name, Ruthie felt like a ball of tangled string.

Her grandma smiled and patted her hand. She whispered, "Now Ruthie, don't think about how you are feeling — instead, think how much I'm going to love hearing you read."

Ruthie's teacher said, "Mary DeLaney wants me to send her some of your stories and poems. If you have something to share with her, put it in this box by tomorrow afternoon."

37D

Ruthie's dad said, "Once I had to read a speech by President Lincoln. I told my mom I was too scared. And your grandma told me, 'David, just stop thinking about yourself all the time!' — so I did, and it worked!"

Ruthie said, "Well, maybe that worked for you, but nothing can help me."

Ruthie's Perfect Poem/Selection 4

At home that night, Ruthie looked in her secret notebook. She chose a poem called "My Couch." It was one of her favorites. Ruthie used her best handwriting and made a copy of the poem.

Ruthie's dad came to her room. He said, "These are some of my old report cards. Take a look."

Ruthie read what the teachers said about her dad. "David needs to speak up in class." "David is a good reader, but he will not read out loud."

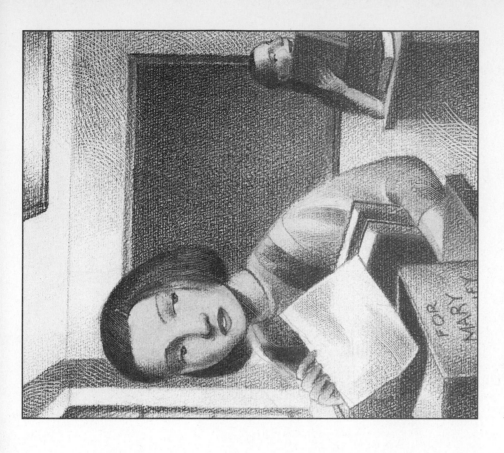

The next day at school, Ruthie waited until she thought no one was watching. Then she put her poem into the box.

At the end of the day, the teacher mailed all the stories and poems to Mary DeLaney.

At home Ruthie told her mom and dad what happened. Her mom said, "That's great! You are such a wonderful writer!"

Ruthie said, "But everyone will be looking at me!"

Then she ran to her room and slammed the door.

Ruthie's Perfect Poem/Selection 4

A week later, Ruthie's class got a letter from Mary DeLaney. The teacher read the letter. Then she said, "This is good news. When Mary DeLaney talks to you and your parents tomorrow night, she wants some of you to read your poems and stories to everyone."

Then the teacher read five names — and first on the list was Ruthie Carter!

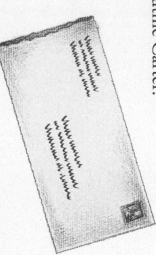

Ruthie worried all day long. She thought, "What if I trip going up to the stage? What if my voice is too soft? What if everyone laughs at me?"

HOUGHTON MIFFLIN

Reading

A Legacy of Literacy

Heroes

THEME 5

Heroes

Reader's Library Selection 1, *Thanks to Sandra Cisneros*
To accompany Anthology Selection 1, *Happy Birthday, Dr. King!*
Comprehension Skill: Cause and Effect

Reader's Library Selection 2, *Duke Ellington: A Life in Music*
To accompany Anthology Selection 2, *Gloria Estefan*
Comprehension Skill: Making Judgments

Reader's Library Selection 3, *Mark McGwire: Home Run Hero*
To accompany Anthology Selection 3, *Lou Gehrig: The Luckiest Man*
Comprehension Skill: Fact and Opinion

Thanks to Sandra Cisneros

by Daniel Santacruz

illustrated by
Kevin Beilfus

Thanks to
Sandra Cisneros

by Daniel Santacruz

illustrated by
Kevin Beilfus

Strategy Focus

What will help Miguel finally write his first poem? As you read, try to **predict** what will happen as Miguel learns about a famous poet.

Think About the Selection

1. Which of Sandra Cisneros's poems does Flora read to Miguel?

2. Why is hearing the Sandra Cisneros poem helpful for Miguel?

3. What makes Flora read the poem to Miguel?

Why It Happened

Copy the chart. Then fill it in for each event.

Cause	Effect
?	Miguel starts to feel nervous.
As a child, Sandra Cisneros couldn't find any books or poems about Mexican people.	?
?	Miguel finally writes a poem about Flora.

Mr. Shaw closed his book and got up from his desk. English class was ending. "Tonight," he told the class, "I want you to write a poem."

"A poem?" Miguel gulped and made a face.

"Yes, Miguel. A poem," said Mr. Shaw. "It can be about anything. You can even write about your sister if you want to."

"A poem about my sister," Miguel laughed to himself. "Who would want to read that?"

When Flora finished reading, she was smiling widely. "That's a nice poem," she said. Then she gave Miguel a hug.

Miguel smiled. Thanks to Flora and Sandra Cisneros, he now knew he could write poems after all.

20

5

3E

Thanks to Sandra Cisneros/Selection 1

When Miguel got home after school, he sat down at his desk. He started to think about the poem. It made him feel nervous. "What can I write a poem about?" Miguel said to himself.

Miguel loved stories, especially mysteries and books with lots of action. But poems were different. The only poems he knew were about flowers or sunsets and things like that. And he lived in the city. What did he know about flowers and sunsets?

Miguel tried to write a poem several times. But each time he started, he stopped before he had finished the first line. It made him feel mad. He crumpled up the piece of paper and tossed it into the garbage pail next to his desk. By now it was filled with white balls of paper.

Finally, Miguel decided to do his math and spelling homework. He would give the poem another try after dinner.

Miguel took the poem to Flora's room. He handed it to her without saying a word. She started to read it.

I've written my first poem to you.
There will not be a poem number two.
You know I'd rather do addition
Than sit and write this composition.

But to you my sister Flora I write
Because you help me do homework at night.
So many spelling words you taught me,
And for the baseball cards you bought me.

I write to say I think you're fine.
I'm glad Flora is a sister of mine!

5E

Thanks to Sandra Cisneros/Selection 1

When dinner was over, Miguel sat at his desk again. He tried writing about a beautiful sunset he had seen over the lake when he had gone swimming last summer. He tried writing about the flowers he gave his Mom for her birthday. He even tried to write about his older sister Flora. But every try ended up in the garbage pail.

When Flora left his room, Miguel knew just what he was going to write about. He walked straight to his desk and grabbed a pencil. The words came easily to him now. He hardly even used his eraser. When he finished, he read the poem over again. He actually liked it!

17

Just then, Miguel's sister Flora came into his room. "Need any help with your spelling or math?" she asked.

Miguel shook his head. "No, I finished that already. Now I have to write a poem."

"A poem about what?" she asked.

"That's just the problem. I don't know," Miguel said.

Flora also told him that when Sandra Cisneros was a child, she couldn't find any books or poems about people whose families were from Mexico. That's why she decided to write about them. She wanted her people to finally see stories and poems about people like themselves.

Thanks to Sandra Cisneros/Selection 1

7E

16

"Poems can be about anything," Flora said. "Just pick something."

"Don't they have to be about things like sunsets or flowers or love?" asked Miguel.

"Wait here a minute," Flora said. "I've got something I want to read to you." Then she ran out of the room.

Miguel asked his sister lots of questions about Sandra Cisneros. Her answers surprised him. He found out that she came from a Mexican family like theirs. Not only that, but she had been born in Chicago too. That's probably why he recognized so much in the poem about the hot dogs. Maybe they had even gone to the same hot dog shop.

Miguel also found out that many of Sandra Cisnero's books and poems were about her own experiences. She wrote about her family and friends and people she knew. And she wrote about other people whose families came from Mexico.

Flora read a few other poems to Miguel. He could see why his sister liked her poems so much. So many of them reminded him of himself and his family.

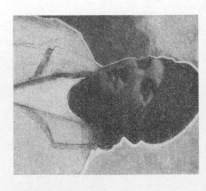

10

15

A minute later Flora appeared again with a worn book in her hand. She quickly flipped through the pages until she came to the one she wanted. "Now listen to this poem. It's called 'Good Hot Dogs,'" she said.

"You mean like the things we eat?" Miguel asked, trying not to laugh.

"Exactly," she said.

Thanks to Sandra Cisneros/Selection 1

14

Flora read the poem slowly. As she read,
a small smile spread across Miguel's mouth.
There were no sunsets or flowers in it. The poem
was just about eating hot dogs. It reminded him
of the Saturdays he and his family went to the
hot dog shop after shopping. Like the poet, he
too liked mustard and onions on his hot dog.
And he laughed when the poem talked about
eating even the little burned pieces of french fries.
He never left a piece on his plate!

When Flora finished reading the poem, she
looked up at Miguel. He was smiling widely.
"Do you see what I mean now?" she asked.
"Exactly," he replied. "By the way, who
wrote the poem?"
"A poet by the name of Sandra Cisneros,"
Flora replied.
"Does she have other poems like that?"
"This book is full of them," she said. "You
can borrow it."

Duke Ellington: A Life In Music

by Erick Montgomery

Duke Ellington:
A Life In Music

by Erick Montgomery

Strategy Focus

How did Duke Ellington change music in America? As you read, **monitor** your reading to make sure you're following the story. Reread any parts you need to **clarify**.

Responding

Think About the Selection

1 Where and when was Duke Ellington born?

2 Why was it important in his career that Duke Ellington moved to New York City when he was 24?

3 Why do you think people loved Duke Ellington's Orchestra so much?

Making Judgments

Copy this chart on a piece of paper. Read the story clues and write a judgment about Duke Ellington.

Story Clue	Judgment
Duke Ellington wrote a new song to play at Carnegie Hall.	Duke knew that playing there required a special song.
With "Black, Brown and Beige," Duke was making his dream of telling the African American story come true.	?

His real name was Edward, but his friends called him Duke. He was born in Washington D.C., in 1899. His talent for music took him far from there. People all over the world came to know Duke Ellington. They knew him for his wonderful, new music and his beautiful smile.

13E

Most people who met Duke Ellington were surprised by how gentle he was. That quiet, elegant man made people happy all over the world. For 50 years, he led the Duke Ellington Orchestra. He made the music that still makes people want to listen, tap their feet, and dance.

Duke Ellington/Selection 2

Duke was seven when he began to play the piano. He liked to play ragtime music. Ragtime was a lively music that sounded strong and fast. Playing ragtime gave Duke his quick fingers. It got him thinking of music all the time. At the age of fourteen he wrote his first song, "Soda Fountain Rag."

Duke began to earn money playing with bands all over Washington. Then, when he was 24, he went to New York City. That's where his music really took off.

Left: Duke Ellington at age four.
Top: The Duke Ellington Orchestra in 1927.

Duke Ellington was the most famous jazz musician of his time. Maybe of all time. He changed popular American music. Musicians all over copied him. He gave them the courage to try new ways of playing and singing music. Even today, young musicians study Duke's music. They dream of someday being as good as Duke was.

Today, musicians like Wynton Marsalis still play Duke's music.

In New York, Duke started his own band, The Duke Ellington Orchestra. An orchestra is a large band with many players playing many different instruments. Duke started his orchestra with twelve players.

By 1927, the Orchestra was playing at Harlem's famous Cotton Club. Duke played piano. He led the band. He also wrote the music. Duke had many big hits. The songs "Mood Indigo" and "Sophisticated Lady" were two of the first.

The Duke Ellington Orchestra also played live on the radio. That made it possible for people all over to hear Duke's music.

President Richard Nixon presents Duke with the Presidential Medal of Freedom.

In 1969, Duke Ellington was given the Presidential Medal of Freedom. That honor is given to special people for service to the United States. Duke Ellington got his award for the years of beautiful music he had given to his country.

Duke was making a new kind of music. He had the players in his band *improvise* as they played. When musicians improvise, they make things up as they play. People were not used to such a bold sound. The Duke Ellington Orchestra became famous for their improvised music.

Another famous player was Louis Armstrong. He was a gifted trumpet player. He sang too. His rough voice and his fantastic trumpet playing gave the Orchestra a New Orleans-style jazz sound. There was no one like Louis Armstrong, either!

Duke Ellington plays with Louis Armstrong.

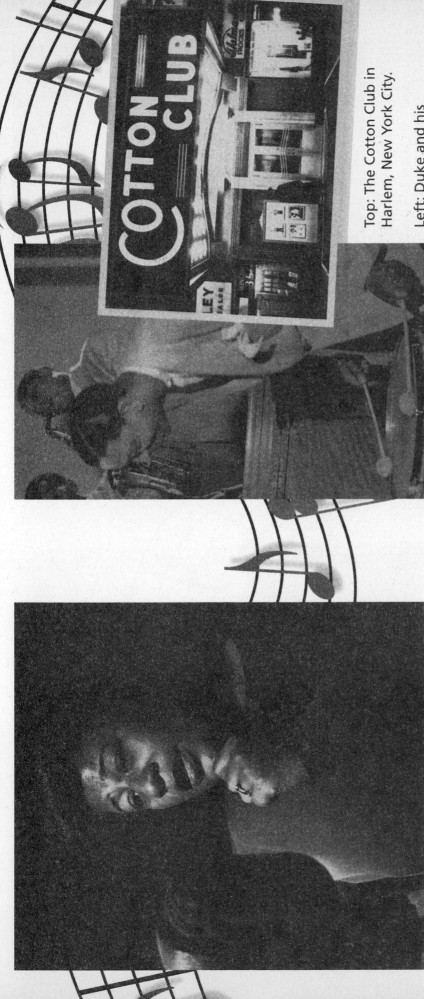

Top: The Cotton Club in Harlem, New York City.

Left: Duke and his improvising Orchestra.

Duke's Orchestra played a fun, fresh kind of music that people loved. It surprised people. It made them move. This music had smooth sounds that thrilled listeners. It had jumpy sounds too.

Ella Fitzgerald sings a song.

It was not just the Duke Ellington Orchestra that people loved. People also wanted to hear the guest singers who sang with the Orchestra. Duke made sure that people got to hear the best. One singer was Ella Fitzgerald. Her singing was like no other. She used her voice as if it were an instrument.

Duke Ellington was at his best when great musicians worked with him. One of the greatest was a songwriter named Billy Strayhorn. When Duke met Billy, Duke knew he had found someone special. Billy became Duke's musical partner in 1939. Over the next forty years, they wrote hundreds of songs together. One was "Take the 'A' Train." It became the Duke Ellington Orchestra's best-known song.

Duke Ellington writes a song with Billy Strayhorn.

Duke's music was a bright light for U.S. soldiers in World War II.

From 1941 to 1945, the United States was fighting World War II. The Duke Ellington Orchestra helped to bring smiles to people's faces in a time of great sadness and worry. Soldiers could listen to his music and think about their families back home listening too. Duke's music was a bright light in a dark time.

In the 1930s and early 1940s, big bands like Duke's were playing a kind of music called *swing*. It was music to tap your feet to. It was music to get up and dance to. People made up new dances to go with the music. The Duke Ellington Orchestra performed swing music all over the United States.

All over America, people danced to swing music.

Duke said that the music he wrote and played was "the voice of his people." And he took that music everywhere. It seemed that everyone who heard his music wanted to hear more and more.

Duke Ellington was famous for his energy. He never tired of writing music. When people asked him what his favorite song was, he liked to answer, "the next five coming up." He would keep writing songs for a long time to come.

Duke Ellington flashes his famous smile.

On January 23, 1943, the Duke Ellington Orchestra played in Carnegie Hall in New York City. Few African Americans had ever played at this beautiful, world-famous concert hall. Duke Ellington had composed, or made up, a new song for this special event.

Duke and his band played his song. It was called "Black, Brown, and Beige." This was not music to dance to. It was a serious work for a big concert hall. Not everyone liked it. But Duke had always dreamed of making music that would tell the story of African Americans in a great way. With "Black, Brown, and Beige," Duke was making this dream come true.

Top: Duke performs at Carnegie Hall.

Right: Duke gets ready for Carnegie Hall.

30

31

20E

MARK McGWIRE: Home Run Hero

by Richard Merchant

illustrated by John Hovell

MARK McGWIRE:
Home Run Hero

by Richard Merchant
illustrated by John Hovell

Strategy Focus

How did Mark McGwire become America's home run hero? As you read, **evaluate** the facts and opinions of this baseball giant.

Responding

Think About the Selection

1 On what date did Mark McGwire break Roger Maris's home run record?

2 What did Mark McGwire give up to be at his son's birth? Why do you think he did that?

3 "During Mark's first year, he was an all-star." Is this a fact or an opinion?

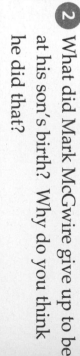

Fact and Opinion

Copy this chart on a piece of paper. Read the sentences from the story. Write whether the sentence is a fact or an opinion.

Clue	Fact or Opinion
He had just made the most famous hit in baseball history.	?
No one on his high school team worked harder.	?
In 1995 Mark slammed 39 home runs.	?

It was September 8, 1998. The giant man in the St. Louis Cardinals uniform gently turned the baseball bat around and around. His huge arms made it look like a toothpick. His eyes were fixed on the Chicago Cubs' pitcher, waiting for the ball. Finally, the pitcher leaned back and threw.

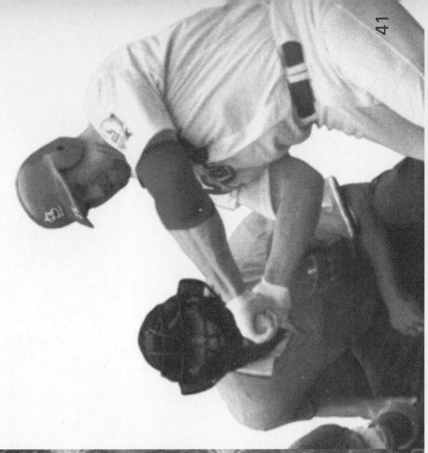

23E

Mark and Sammy Sosa both had great years in 1998. They both broke the existing home run record. But at the end of the season, Mark finally came out on top. He had hit an amazing 70 home runs. That record may never be broken. It shows what's possible if you work hard, stay focused, and don't give up.

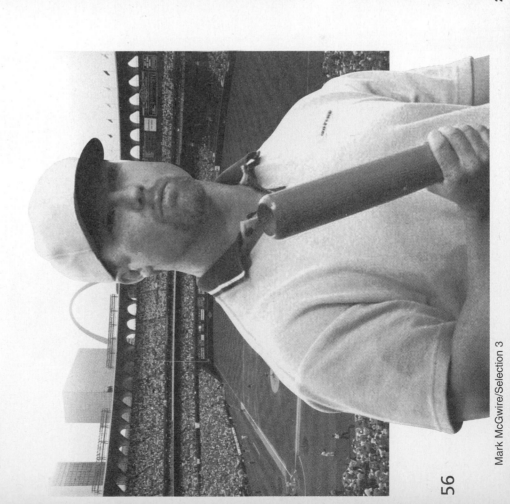

Mark McGwire/Selection 3

Mark McGwire hits number 62!

CRACK! The baseball popped off the end of the bat and screamed towards the outfield. It looked as if the ball was going to bounce off the wall. But it kept going just enough to clear the wall — a home run! Everyone in the crowd jumped to their feet and started cheering wildly. It was the most exciting day of the 1998 season.

The next year Mark started hitting a lot of home runs for the Cardinals. But now he had another problem. Sammy Sosa, a player for the Chicago Cubs, was also hitting a lot of home runs. All season long, they challenged each other for the league lead. Still, they stayed friendly. The competition made them both play better.

Sammy Sosa

The huge man who hit the ball was Mark McGwire. It was his 62nd home run of the season. He had hit far longer home runs that year. This one, however, was the most important. This one broke the record of 61 home runs in a season set by Roger Maris in 1961. The great Babe Ruth held the record before that with 60 home runs way back in 1927.

Roger Maris

Mark would need to focus all he could the next year. He started the season by hitting 34 homers for the A's. Then, on July 31, Mark was traded to the St. Louis Cardinals. Still, he kept hitting home runs. Now, it was getting harder for Mark to concentrate. Before and after each game, reporters hounded him with questions. "Will you break the record this year?" they asked. Mark came close. He hit 58 home runs that season.

25E

Mark was so excited that he almost forgot to touch first base! All of the ballplayers on the field congratulated him as he circled the bases. When he crossed home plate, he ran straight to his son Matthew. He lifted him up in the air in front of the cheering crowd. The usually calm Mark was grinning from ear to ear. He had just made the most famous hit in baseball history.

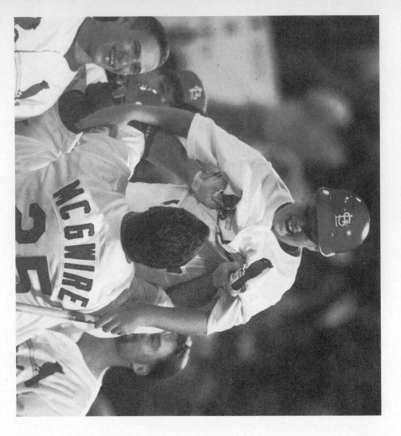

In 1995 Mark slammed 39 home runs. He did this even though he played only part of the season because of injuries. In 1996 he did even better, pounding 53 home runs. Now other pitchers were afraid of him. He was a star again.

Many fans wondered how Mark improved so much. He knew the answer. He had learned how to focus and concentrate.

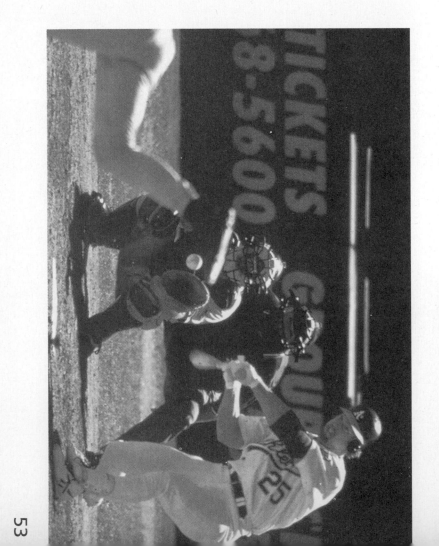

26E

As Mark stood there, it was hard to imagine he had ever had problems playing baseball. Few people knew that while growing up, Mark's poor eyesight had caused him a lot of trouble. But even as a young boy, Mark was never one to let problems stand in his way. He just kept trying.

45

By now Mark was thinking of quitting. Everyone thought he would never be as good as he had been. But while Mark was injured, he didn't give up. He began watching all the pitchers very carefully. He studied their pitches, hoping it would help him for the next season.

52

27E

Mark played on the 1984 U.S. Olympic team.

Mark worked hard to make himself a star player in school. No one on his high school team worked harder. Later in college, he set the first of his home run records. The hard work paid off. He was chosen to play major league baseball by both the Oakland A's and New York Mets. Mark picked the A's so he could live closer to his family in California.

In 1992, things seemed to look up for Big Mac. He hit 42 home runs that year and started playing better. He was hoping the next year he would improve even more. But then he got injured and missed much of the season. He got injured again the next year too. Things were going from bad to worse.

During his first full season in the majors, Mark made history right away. He hit 49 home runs to lead the American League! It was the most home runs ever hit by a player in his first year. Mark could have hit even more, but he decided not to play the last three games of the year. Instead he wanted to be at his son's birth. "You'll always have a chance to hit 50 home runs," Mark told reporters later.

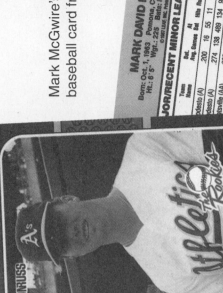

Mark McGwire's rookie baseball card from 1987

Mark tried to figure out how to become a better hitter. He tried standing closer to home plate. That meant he might get hit by a pitch. Mark thought it would make it easier for him to hit the ball.

Still his hitting kept getting worse. So did his vision. Other players and coaches tried to tell him what he was doing wrong. But nothing worked.

During Mark's first year, he was an all-star. Everyone expected him to get even better the next year. Maybe they made him nervous or maybe he tried too hard. But in his second year, he hit only 32 homers.

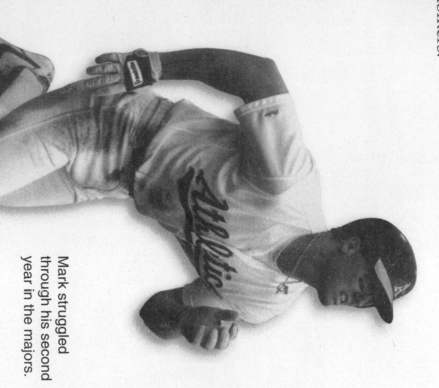

Mark struggled through his second year in the majors.

Even though Mark was still a good player, the fans and the press were disappointed. They wanted him to be a star. By the middle of the 1988 season, Mark started to become angry with reporters and fans. He thought they expected too much from such a young player. But inside Mark wanted to do better too.

HOUGHTON MIFFLIN

Reading

A Legacy of Literacy

Nature: Friend and Foe

THEME 6

Nature: Friend and Foe

Reader's Library Selection 1, *Peter's Harvest*
To accompany Anthology Selection 1, *Salmon Summer*
Comprehension Skill: Following Directions

Reader's Library Selection 2, *Landslides*
To accompany Anthology Selection 2, *Wildfires*
Comprehension Skill: Topic, Main Idea and Supporting Details

Reader's Library Selection 3, *Whiteout*
To accompany Anthology Selection 3, *Skylark*
Comprehension Skill: Making Inferences

Peter's Harvest

by Anne Sibley O'Brien

illustrated by John F. Martin

1F

Peter's Harvest

by Anne Sibley O'Brien

illustrated by John F. Martin

Strategy Focus

How will Peter learn the family tradition of harvesting wild rice? As you read, stop and **summarize** each part of the story.

2F

Responding

Think About the Selection

1 What do the Ojibwe call wild rice?

2 Why is it important that Peter learn the family tradition of harvesting wild rice?

3 What are the steps for harvesting wild rice?

Following Directions

Copy this chart on a piece of paper. Write directions that tell how to "finish" wild rice.

Directions for "finishing" wild rice

1. First the wild rice is spread on plastic sheets. The sun dries it.

2. _____ ?

3. _____ ?

4. _____ ?

5. _____ ?

A rich, smoky smell rose from Peter's plate. Peter looked closely at the grains of rice. Each grain had split open. They looked as if they had golden wings. Peter tasted a spoonful. He let the nutty flavor roll around in his mouth.

"Is it good?" asked his mother.

Peter nodded. This rice was better than good. For Peter, it was special in a way that was hard to describe.

The Ojibwe have many stories about the great hero Manabozho. Long, long ago, Manabozho's people used to go hungry during the cold winters. Manabozho prayed and fasted, but no dream came to show him how to help his people. Then, by a lake, Manabozho did have an important dream. He saw dancers swaying gracefully. He danced with them. When he awoke, he saw that the dancers were wild grasses. Birds came to eat the grains that fell from the grasses. Manabozho brought the good news to his people. Food was all around them, waiting to be harvested.

Now, there it was on Peter's family's table — the delicious wild rice called *manoomin*.

Peter had been eating this kind of rice his whole life. But at this meal, he was eating rice he had helped to pick, or *harvest*. Maybe that was why the rice seemed so wonderful.

Wild rice was the name English-speaking people used for this food. To them, the thin grain looked like rice. Peter's people, the Ojibwe (Oh-**jib**-way), called it *manoomin*. Manoomin was a grass. It grew wild, and its seeds gave life.

Next, the grains were tossed gently until the husk pieces blew away in the wind.

At last, the rice was ready to be cooked. Cooking was the easiest and fastest step of all.

Hundreds of years ago, the Ojibwe came to the lands around the upper Great Lakes. Wild grass grew in the lakes and rivers. The Ojibwe learned that grains from the grass could be made into good food. They learned when it was best to harvest the grain and how to prepare the grain for eating.

Ojibwe Homelands

(The Ojibwe also use the names Chippewa and Anishinaabe.)

As parents passed down their learning to their children, they also told stories about manoomin. They told how their great hero, Manabozho (Man-a-**bo**-zo), had helped them find it.

Today, many Ojibwe live in the homelands of their ancestors. Some Ojibwe still harvest manoomin in the old way.

18

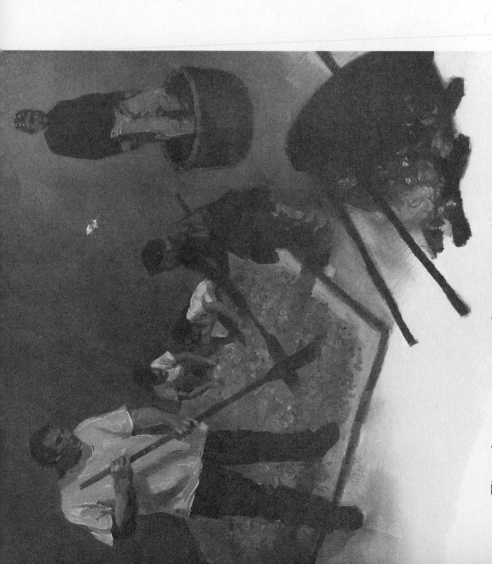

First the rice was spread on plastic sheets. The sun began to dry it out.

After that, the rice was stirred in a big metal pot over a low fire. The rice dried more.

Then Grandfather "danced" on the rice. Grind, grind, grind—slowly, the rice husks broke away from the grains.

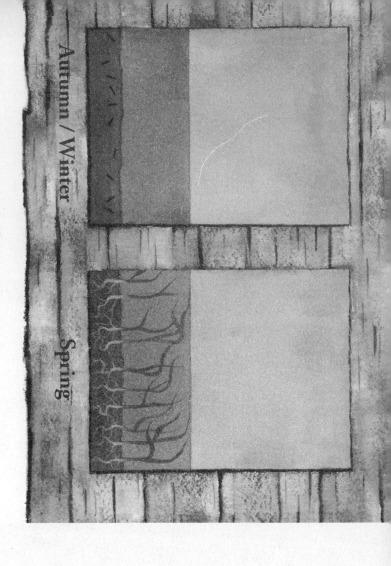

Autumn / Winter

Spring

Throughout the fall and winter, grains of wild rice lie in the mud under water. In the spring, the melting snows bring floods. The moving water stirs up the mud. The rice grains begin to send out roots. As the roots grow into plants, they begin climbing toward the sun.

By early summer, the stalks are poking up from the water. Flowers appear. The stalks and leaves grow taller and taller. By late summer, the plants are three feet above the water.

When Grandfather suggested a break, Peter agreed right away. He was tired! They rested and talked with friends. Then Peter and his grandfather switched places.

Peter tried using the knockers. At first, he couldn't get at the right part of the stalks. Then he knocked the grains everywhere but into the canoe. When they hit his face, they itched terribly. He kept trying, and slowly he improved.

It was nearly noon when Peter and his grandfather landed with a full canoe. They poured their rice into bags and headed home. It was time to "finish" the rice. There were still many steps to take.

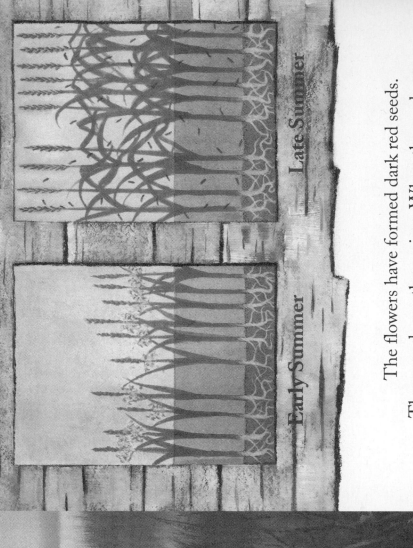

Early Summer   Late Summer

9

The flowers have formed dark red seeds. These seeds are the grains. When the seeds are ripe, they fall off into the water. They drift down into the mud where they will grow in the next spring.

The ripe seeds are ready to fall in late August and early September. That is the time for harvesting.

16

7F

Quickly, Grandfather used his other arm to grab another bunch. Again and again, Grandfather knocked with one stick, then the other. Peter listened to the *swish, rap, swish, rap*. It was like a song without words. The pile of rice grew larger.

This season, Peter's family drove to their usual spot for ricing. Peter looked out at the lake. It was like a field of grass. He looked into the bright blue sky. He saw a few ducks flying in the distance. They were enjoying harvest time too.

Peter's mother and grandfather took the canoe out. They had been ricing together ever since Peter could remember. Harvesting was a job for two people. One person stood and poled the canoe. The other person sat and used sticks to knock the grains of rice into the canoe.

Peter always looked forward to the rice harvest. It was a time to play with his cousins. They also came to the lake with their parents.

"You've got the hang of it now," Grandfather told Peter after a while. The sun felt hot. Poling was hard work. But Peter felt good about the steady way he was moving the canoe.

While Peter steered, Grandfather used the sticks called *knockers*. He held a knocker in each hand. First he wrapped an arm and a stick around a bunch of stalks. Then he bent the stalks over the side of the canoe. Using the stick in his other hand, he knocked the tops of the stalks. The grains flew off. Most of them landed in the canoe bottom. Some landed in the water. Those would have a chance to make new plants for the next season.

On the third morning of harvesting, Peter awoke before anyone else. He dressed quickly. Outside, the sky was beginning to glow with the rising sun. Peter could see his breath in the chilly air. This was the morning he had been waiting for. Today, he would take a turn as Grandfather's ricing partner.

Peter and his grandfather slipped the canoe into the water. Peter stood with the tall pole. Grandfather sat in front of him.

"We'll start out slowly," said Grandfather. Peter stuck the pole into the mud and pushed off. The canoe moved forward. It also tipped to one side. Peter steadied himself. Standing in a moving canoe was not easy.

Landslides

by Linda Hartley

Landslides

by Linda Hartley

Strategy Focus

What happens when tons of rocks and dirt slide down a mountain? **Monitor** your reading as you go. Reread to **clarify** parts that you don't understand.

Responding

Think About the Selection

1. What happens in a landslide?
2. What are two causes of landslides?
3. Give some supporting details that show how earthquakes make landslides happen.

SLIDE AREA

Main Idea/Supporting Details

Copy this chart on a piece of paper. Write two supporting details for the second main idea.

Main Idea	Supporting Details
Many landslides are caused by natural erosion.	1. Wind and water wear away rocks and soil. 2. Rain and melting snow cause rocks and soil to loosen.
Geologists use maps and photos to study landslides.	1. ? 2. ?

A rock climber moves up the side of Washington Column.

I t was a warm July evening in Yosemite National Park. A rock climber slowly made his way up Washington Column. Suddenly he heard a CRACK! "That sounds like thunder," he thought. But when he turned his head, there was no storm. The noise had come from the side of a nearby mountain.

A giant landslide at Red Mountain in the San Juan Mountains of Colorado

Some landslides are caused by changes people make to the earth's surface. Most are caused by erosion, volcanoes, and earthquakes. Either way, landslides are both terrible disasters and thrilling events that shape our ever-changing world.

CRACK! BOOM! Giant boulders bounced down the side of Glacier Point. "I just stood there with my mouth open," the rock climber said afterward.

Later he learned that 162,000 tons of rock had rushed down the mountain. They had traveled at about 160 miles an hour. Fourteen people were hurt. One person died. The rock climber had seen a huge landslide.

Inset: A landslide roars down a slope.

Geologists are always looking for new ways to study landslides. They get better at predicting where and when landslides might happen. By keeping track of landslides, geologists can protect people from these dangerous natural events.

A landslide happens when large amounts of rocks and soil move from a high place to a lower place. Visitors to Yosemite don't often see landslides. A long time may pass between landslides. But the work of landslides can be seen all over Yosemite — and all over the world. For millions of years, landslides have changed the surface of the earth.

The view from Glacier Point of Half Dome in Yosemite

When engineers and builders make plans, they study the land. They get helpful information from geologists about where landslides might happen. They can then decide where to build — or not to build — roads, hospitals, homes, and schools.

As builders clear land for houses, the safest sites get used first. Before long, houses are built on areas that aren't safe. But geologists warn that some places are just too dangerous for building. Landslides can bury a house in moments. Even a beautiful view isn't worth being buried in a landslide.

The giant mudslide in the photo on the right ripped apart homes on this hill in California.

15F

36

Landslides/Selection 2

Many landslides are caused by natural erosion. Wind and water wear away rocks and soil over time. Heavy rains and melting snow cause rocks and soil to loosen. If the land is steep, a landslide may happen. The landslide at Glacier Point was probably caused by natural erosion.

Before

After

The two diagrams show what happens during a landslide.

Landslides can be a big danger to houses built near hills. Many people enjoy living with beautiful views. So they live in houses on top of hills. But if a landslide happens, the ground can come out from under these homes. They can go sliding downhill. Or a landslide can send tons of rocks crashing down on houses at the bottom of hills.

Builders are finding new, safer ways to build near hills. They cut back into hillsides. Then they remove the loose rocks and soil that could slide into houses.

The houses on the side of this hill in Hollywood, California, could come crashing down if a landslide were to happen.

35

Geologists are people who study the earth. They know that landslides happen more often in some places than in others. Geologists look at rocks and soil and underground water. They measure slopes. They can often tell *where* a landslide is likely to happen. But geologists can't always tell *when* it will happen.

Most landslides are too fast, powerful, and dangerous to study in action. But there is one landslide of special interest. It moves very slowly, all the time. It is called the Slumgullion landslide. Its name means "watery meat stew."

Three scientists look down a landslide in the state of Washington.

Clear-cutting can leave huge areas without trees.

Another way people cause landslides is by clear-cutting. Clear-cutting is the chopping down of all the trees in one area. This gets rid of the tree roots that once held rocks and soil in place. Without the roots, rain can then wash rocks and soil down slopes in a landslide. In Oregon, many people believe that landslides are getting worse because there is too much clear-cutting.

The Slumgullion landslide today

The huge Slumgullion landslide is in Colorado. Geologists can study how this landslide flows because it moves so slowly. Parts of the Slumgullion have been moving downward for 300 years. Like the fast landslide at Yosemite, this slow landslide is also caused by natural erosion.

Geologists use maps and photos to study landslides like the Slumgullion. Maps are made with the help of satellites circling the earth. Photos are taken from airplanes. Today's photos and maps are compared with old photos and maps. Geologists can see how the land has been changed.

Landslides are possible on the sides of many roads because of the way the roads were built. Workers blast away hills to build roads. The blasting leaves steep slopes. The steeper the slopes, the greater the chance that rocks and soil will fall in a landslide. Road signs that say "Watch Out for Falling Rock" warn of the chance of a landslide.

Nowadays, road builders can do several things to prevent landslides. Sometimes they fix rocks in place with large bolts. Sometimes they use wire fences to keep falling rocks from landing on the road below. The important thing is to stop the rocks before they fall.

Some landslides are caused by volcanoes. When a volcano erupts, tons of rocks and dirt can go flying down its sides. The volcano's power can create huge, deadly landslides.

In 1980 the Mount Saint Helens volcano in Washington erupted. A side of the mountain broke away in a great explosion. Lava and hot gases poured out. Ash, rocks, and soil formed a mighty landslide. It tore down millions of trees. Everything in the landslide's path was destroyed.

The Mount Saint Helens volcano erupting in 1980

19F

Large fences are used to keep landslides from falling onto roads.

SLIDE AREA

Natural erosion, volcanoes, and earthquakes all cause landslides. Some landslides, however, have a different cause — people. When people change the surface of the earth, landslides are often the result.

Landslides/Selection 2

The Mount Saint Helens landslide seemed huge when it happened. But a landslide more than six times as large has been found underwater in the Atlantic Ocean. It happened many thousands of years ago. Its cause was an underwater volcano.

Underwater volcanoes have caused the largest landslides ever found. In the Pacific Ocean near Hawaii, scientists have found huge rock slides. Some of the rocks have moved over 100 miles from the volcanic mountain where they first fell. How did a landslide travel so far underwater? Scientists are still trying to find out.

Earthquakes are another force that can set off landslides. When large parts of the earth suddenly move, everything on the surface moves too. That is what happens in an earthquake. Rocks and soil are pushed loose from cliffs, roadsides, and slopes. All this stuff goes falling down as landslides.

The landslides caused by earthquakes are very powerful. In Montana in 1959, an earthquake caused an entire mountainside to slide into the Madison River.

By looking closely at areas where earthquakes often happen, geologists try to make predictions about landslides. They usually can tell where landslides are likely to happen in earthquake zones.

This gigantic crack in the earth was caused by an earthquake. The same power can cause large landslides.

WHITEOUT

by Kay Livorse
illustrated by Dave Kramer

WHITEOUT

by Kay Livorse
illustrated by Dave Kramer

Strategy Focus

Will a big blizzard bring big trouble for
Mary Alice's family? As you read, try to
predict what will happen next.

22F

Responding

Think About the Selection

1 Where did Robert grow up?

2 When Mary Alice wakes up, why is
she startled by the silence?

3 How can you tell that Charlie's
feelings about Robert are changing?

Making Inferences

Copy this chart on a piece of paper. Then use the
clues to make inferences.

What the author tells us:	What you can infer:
a. Mary Alice and Charlie race downstairs.	a. The children want to play in the snow.
b. "Great," said Charlie with a frown. "Look who made it home last night."	b. ?
c. Charlie tells Robert he doesn't need any help.	c. ?

When Mary Alice woke up, she was startled by . . . silence. She heard no dogs barking, no traffic on the street. Where was the train whistle that usually woke her? Everything seemed so calm and quiet.

Mary Alice jumped up and looked out the window. Snow! Everywhere she looked. The whole world outside was white as . . . well, snow!

She ran into the next room to tell her brother Charlie the good news. She jumped on his bed to wake him up.

They all rode in the ambulance with Charlie. Mary Alice could see Charlie staring at Robert. "You're not so bad after all," Charlie finally spoke up. "For a guy from Vermont."

Robert grinned and said, "Well, Charlie, I guess once you get to know me, I'm not all bad."

And the whole family smiled as the ambulance cut through the white walls of snow.

23F

Mary Alice and Charlie raced downstairs. Mom and Robert were already making breakfast. Charlie headed for the door to the yard.

"Whoa!" said Robert. "Breakfast before play, Sport."

Robert was their stepfather. Their real father had died when Charlie was five. Mom had married Robert last year. Mary Alice had warmed to Robert right away. Charlie was still getting used to having someone in his dad's place.

"Great," said Charlie with a frown. "Look who made it home last night."

"Did you have trouble on the roads, Robert?" Mary Alice asked.

Robert had been a player for the Cleveland Browns football team. Now he was a police officer. He often worked late into the night.

"Got a ride just in time!" said Robert.

"With all this snow, the roads will be closed for days. Plows can barely keep up."

Mom was getting to the good part. Then, all of a sudden, they heard a rumbling noise outside. It was a snowplow, followed by an ambulance!

Out of the plow jumped Robert. Robert walked into the house with the ambulance driver. Mary Alice saw Charlie crack a small smile.

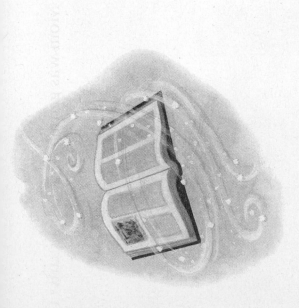

Mary Alice kept getting more snow for Charlie's leg. Mom made peanut butter sandwiches for lunch. Charlie tried not to think about his leg.

"Do you think Robert can get someone to help?" Charlie asked.

"Yes," said Mary Alice. "I think Robert can do just about anything."

Mom smiled and started to read them a mystery story to pass the time.

25F

They all watched Robert bundle up and strap on the snowshoes. Mary Alice thought he looked like he had tennis rackets on his feet.

"Be back with help in a jiff, Sport," Robert said to Charlie. "Everything'll be okay." Then he disappeared into the blowing white storm.

Mom held up her hand. "Listen! They're talking about the storm on the radio," she said.

"Six hours into the blizzard and no end in sight. Folks, we've got a whiteout here. A record snowfall for eastern Ohio! People are warned to stay — " The radio went dead. The lights went out too.

"Yippee! Power's out!" said Charlie. "Who needs lights in the day, anyway?"

"Got plenty of coal in the cellar, though," Robert added. "At least the house'll keep warm."

But right now Mary Alice and Charlie didn't really care about a warm house. They had snowmen on their minds. They gobbled up their eggs and ran to the door.

"Mom, can we go out and play now?" Charlie asked.

"Sure," said Mom, "but dress warmly. Hats *and mittens.*"

Robert grinned and reached into the coat closet.

"What are those things?" he asked.

"Snowshoes!" said Robert. "They let you walk in deep snow. Growing up in Vermont, I used my snowshoes all winter long."

For a moment, Charlie forgot about his pain.

52

Whiteout/Selection 3

27F

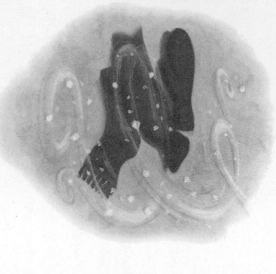

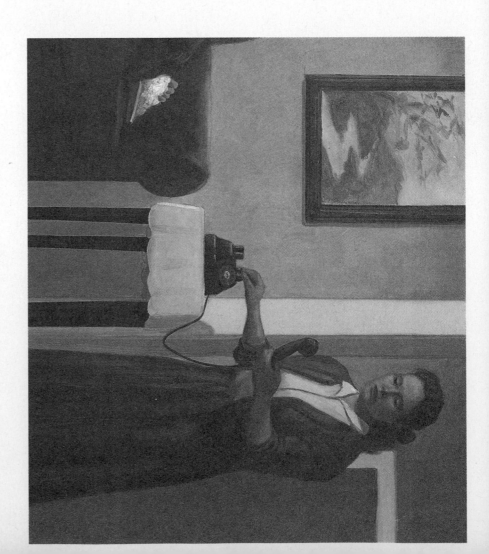

M ary Alice and Charlie dashed out the back door into the white swirl of snow.

"Stay in the yard," called Robert.

"Yes, boss," Charlie replied. The door slammed behind him.

Mary Alice had never seen such deep snow. She and Charlie flopped around in the drifts. They tried to build a snowman. They laughed and threw snowballs. Then Charlie headed toward the toolshed. He started to climb up on one side.

"Keep Charlie on ice," said Robert. "I'll walk to the police station. There's a hospital on the same street. I'll bet that street has been plowed. I'll find a doctor or something . . ."

"But that's miles away!" said Mary Alice. "How can you walk that far in this deep snow?"

"Hey!" shouted Mary Alice. "What are you doing up there?"

"Look at me! I'm Super — " yelled Charlie. Before he finished the word, he jumped. He held his arms out like a superhero. But instead of flying, he flopped. Right into a huge drift of snow.

"Owwww!!" Charlie screamed from under a white pile. Mary Alice couldn't see him.

"Charlie!" cried Mary Alice. She tried to run to him. But the deep snow made it hard.

"I'll get a pan and fill it with snow," said Mary Alice.

"Great idea," said Robert. "Snow will work fine."

Mom tried to call the doctor, but the phone was dead too. "What'll we do now?" she asked.

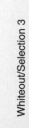

29F

Whiteout/Selection 3

48

"My leg!" moaned Charlie. Now Mary Alice could see her brother under the pile of snow. He was crying and holding his right leg.

Robert rushed out the back door. He'd heard Charlie's scream. He plowed through the snow towards Charlie's red snow hat.

"What's the deal there, Sport?" he called to Charlie. Robert could barely get through the snow too. But he made it to Charlie before Mary Alice.

Charlie saw Robert coming. "I'll be all right," he said. "I don't need any help." He tried to stand. His leg hurt so much he almost passed out. He fell back into the snow.

Robert picked Charlie up and carried him into the house without a word. Mary Alice followed. She saw that Charlie was in too much pain to talk. She knew he didn't want to, anyway.

Robert took off Charlie's boots and gently felt his lower leg. Mary Alice could see that the limb was swollen. Tears filled Charlie's eyes. Robert frowned. "Looks kind of like a broken leg there, Sport," said Robert. "Some ice on it will keep it from swelling more."

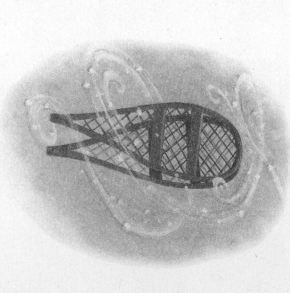

49

HOUGHTON MIFFLIN
Reading
A Legacy of Literacy

Reader's Library
Blackline Masters

PQM203924

ISBN 0-618-06713-2

9 780618 067138

90000 >

1-43454-**LV 4**

 HOUGHTON MIFFLIN